2008
Self-Catering Holidays

In Britain
With Caravans and Camping Sites

Maps: ©MAPS IN MINUTES™ / Collins Bartholomew 2007

Typeset by FHG Guides Ltd, Paisley.
Printed and bound in Malaysia by Imago.

Distribution. Book Trade: ORCA Book Services, Stanley House,
3 Fleets Lane, Poole, Dorset BH15 3AJ
(Tel: 01202 665432; Fax: 01202 666219)
e-mail: mail@orcabookservices.co.uk
Published by FHG Guides Ltd., Abbey Mill Business Centre,
Seedhill, Paisley PA1 ITJ (Tel: 0141-887 0428 Fax: 0141-889 7204).
e-mail: admin@fhguides.co.uk

Self-Catering Holidays is published by FHG Guides Ltd,
part of Kuperard Group.

Cover design: FHG Guides
Cover Pictures: With thanks to
right; Searles Leisure Resort, Hunstanton, Norfolk, (see details on page 64).
left; Lakeland Country Cottages, Keswick, Cumbria, (see details on page 102).

 Totally non-smoking
 Children Welcome
Suitable for Disabled Guests

 Pets Welcome
 Short Breaks
 Licensed

Contents

LEGOLAND® WINDSOR SCORES A 'MOLE-IN-ONE'

A new 18-hole mini-golf attraction called 'Mole-In-One' has opened at LEGOLAND® Windsor. The woodland-themed course includes LEGO® brick models of squirrels, foxes, moles and otters as well as beautiful water features set in a stunning landscaped location.

Each hole has a different woodland animal theme and like all of the park's attractions, they focus on interactive, hands-on entertainment. There is even a special 'Heroes Hole' just for younger golfers so playing against an adult couldn't be more fun!

The new course is located in the DUPLO® Land area of the park and during the peak season 'Mole-In-One' can be separated into two nine hole courses to reduce waiting times. One of the nine hole courses is fully wheelchair accessible.

National leisure contractor, Western Log Group, was commissioned to build the £300,000 outdoor attraction and this latest addition to the Berkshire theme park is a joint venture project between two companies.

Vicky Brown, general manager of LEGOLAND® Windsor commented: "Our attractions are all about interacting and learning through play. The Mole-In-One mini-golf course allows children to practice new skills and have fun with their families at the same time so fits perfectly into a day here at the park."

visit www.legoland.co.uk

Other specialised holiday guides from **FHG**

Recommended **INNS & PUBS** OF BRITAIN Recommended • **COUNTRY HOTELS** OF BRITAIN

Recommended **SHORT BREAK HOLIDAYS** IN BRITAIN

The bestselling and original **PETS WELCOME!**

The GOLF GUIDE, *Where to Play, Where to Stay* IN BRITAIN & IRELAND

COAST & COUNTRY HOLIDAYS • **CARAVAN & CAMPING HOLIDAYS** IN BRITAIN

BED & BREAKFAST STOPS • **CHILDREN WELCOME!** Family Holiday & Days Out Guide

BRITAIN'S BEST LEISURE & RELAXATION GUIDE

Published annually: available in all good bookshops or direct from the publisher:

FHG Guides, Abbey Mill Business Centre, Seedhill, Paisley PA1 1TJ

Tel: 0141 887 0428 • Fax: 0141 889 7204

E-mail: admin@fhguides.co.uk • Web: www.holidayguides.com

Win a

Snooper **Strabo**
2 in 1 Speed Camera locator and Satellite Navigation System

Here's your chance to win the most technologically advanced driving aid in Europe, a **STRABO** 2 in 1 Speed Camera locator and Satellite Navigation System, from the leading satellite navigation brand, **Snooper.**

Snooper Strabo combines speed camera location technology with Navteqs excellent premium street level mapping. The easy to use, stylish system benefits from a built in re-chargeable battery. It has a speed camera monitoring function and will also locate designated accident hotspots and high-risk zones provided by Snooper's unique Enigma speed camera database, which can be updated daily.

Strabo can also be programmed quickly via its LCD touch screen by either inputting a postcode or searching a city or town. It also benefits from up to seven different search methods and extensive lists of Points of Interest, as well as a MP 3 player. Normally priced at £199.99 for the UK and Ireland mapping and £249.99 for the European version.

You can win one of these by answering this simple question:
How many different search methods does Snooper Strabo have?

Name ....

Address ....

....

Postcode ....Date...........................

To enter, cut out this slip and return to FHG GUIDES LTD, FREEPOST SCO2623, PAISLEY PA1 1BR
Closing date 31ST OCTOBER 2008

For more information please visit www.snooperuk.com or call Performance Products on 0870 787 070

England

England and Wales · Counties

Unitary Authorities – England & Wales

1. Plymouth
2. Torbay
3. Poole
4. Bournemouth
5. Southampton
6. Portsmouth
7. Brighton & Hove
8. Medway
9. Thurrock
10. Southend
11. Slough
12. Windsor & Maidenhead
13. Bracknell Forest
14. Wokingham
15. Reading
16. West Berkshire
17. Swindon
18. Bath & Northeast Somerset
19. North Somerset
20. Bristol
21. South Gloucestershire
22. Luton
23. Milton Keynes
24. Peterborough
25. Leicester
26. Nottingham
27. Derby
28. Telford & Wrekin
29. Stoke-on-Trent
30. Warrington
31. Halton
32. Merseyside
33. Blackburn with Darwen
34. Blackpool
35. N.E. Lincolnshire
36. North Lincolnshire
37. Kingston-upon-Hull
38. York
39. Redcar & Cleveland
40. Middlesborough
41. Stockton-on-Tees
42. Darlington
43. Hartlepool

NORTH WALES
a. Denbighshire
b. Flintshire
c. Wrexham

SOUTH WALES
d. Swansea
e. Neath & Port Talbot
f. Bridgend
g. Rhondda Cynon Taff
h. Merthyr Tydfil
i. Vale of Glamorgan
j. Cardiff
k. Caerphilly
l. Blaenau Gwent
m. Torfaen
n. Newport
o. Monmouthshire

Visit the FHG website

www.holidayguides.com

for details of the wide choice of accommodation

featured in the full range of FHG titles

Cornwall

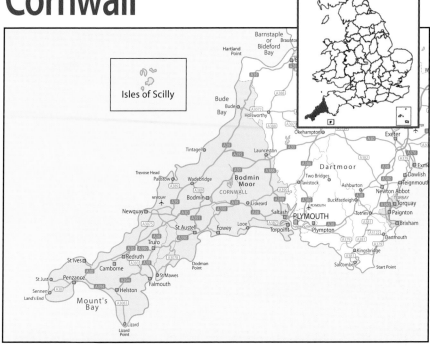

Bodmin, Bude

Bude, Crackington Haven, Cusgarne (near Truro)

Fowey, Gorran Haven, Helford River, Launceston

Looe, Looe Valley, Marazion

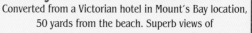

MARAZION near. Mrs W. Boase, Trebarvah Farm, Trebarvah Lane, Perranuthnoe, Penzance TR20 9NG (01736 710361)
Trebarvah Farm Cottages. Four cottages with magnificent views across Mount's Bay and St Michael's Mount. Just east of Marazion, Perranuthnoe is easily accessible on foot or by car and has a sandy beach. Accommodation – TUE BROOK: one double and two twin-bedded rooms, one en suite, kitchen/diner, lounge and large conservatory. TAIRUA: one double and one twin-bedded room and a livingroom. KERIKERI COTTAGE: one twin room and a double sofa bed in the livingroom. COROMANDEL: one double en suite, one twin bedroom, double sofa bed in living room. All properties include duvets, pillows and blankets but no linen or towels. Kitchens are electric and power is through a pre-payment £1 coin meter. Colour TV.
Rates: from £200 to £545 per week.
• Two cottages sleeping four people, two sleeping up to six people. • Open Easter to October.
e-mail: jaybee@trebarvah.freeserve.co.uk　　　www.trebarvahfarmcottages.co.uk

SB

Truro

Devon

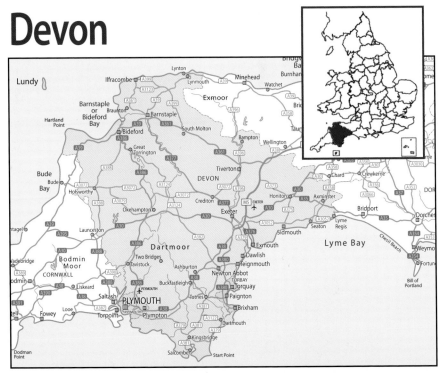

symbols

	Totally non-smoking		Pets Welcome
	Children Welcome	**SB**	Short Breaks
	Suitable for Disabled Guests		Licensed

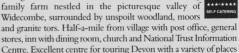

Axminster, Barnstaple, Brixham

Westward Ho!

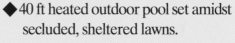

West Anstey, Woolacombe

symbols

⊘ Totally non-smoking

🐴 Children Welcome

♿ Suitable for Disabled Guests

 Pets Welcome

SB Short Breaks

🍷 Licensed

Dorset

Wells

Warminster

Glastonbury

Shepton Mallet

Street

SOMERSET

Wincanton

Langport

Shaftesbury

Ilminster

Yeovil

Sherborne

Chard

Crewkerne

Blandford Forum

Ringwood

SOUTHAMPTO

Lyndhurst

New Forest

Axminster

Wimborne Minster

New Milton

Brocken

DORSET

Bridport

Dorchester

POOLE

Poole

BOURNE MOUTH

Christchurch

Lyme Regis

Seaton

Wareham

Bournemouth

Freshwater

Poole Bay

Lyme Bay

Chesil Beach

Weymouth

Swanage

Isle o
Wig

Fortuneswell

Bill of Portland

Sandbanks, Dorset. Picture courtesy of Poole Tourism

DORSET COTTAGE HOLIDAYS

Large selection of graded self-catering cottages, bungalows, town houses and apartments, all within 10 miles of the heritage coastline and sandy beaches. Excellent walking in idyllic countryside, pets welcome. All fully modernised retaining many olde features, open fires and exposed beams and enjoying panoramic views of coastline and countryside. Open all year, 1 to 4 bedrooms, sleeping from 2-10 guests. From £135 per week per cottage. Short breaks available.

Free brochure: 01929 553443
Email: enq@dhcottages.co.uk • www.dhcottages.co.uk

Beaminster, Blandford Forum

Orchard End & The Old Coach House
Hooke, Beaminster.

Hooke is a quiet village nine miles from the coast. Good walking country and near Hooke Working Woodland with lovely woodland walks. Coarse fishing nearby.

Orchard End is a stone-built bungalow, with electric central heating and double glazing. Four bedrooms, two bathrooms; sleeps 8. Well-equipped and comfortable. Enclosed garden and off-road parking.

The Old Coach House, a cottage sleeping 9, is also finished to a high standard. Four bedrooms, two bathrooms; central heating. Large garden; off-road parking. Both properties (on a working dairy farm) are equipped with washing machine, dryer, dishwasher, fridge/freezers, microwaves and payphones. Both properties **ETC** ★★★★

Terms from £300 to £750 inclusive of VAT, electricity, bed linen and towels.

enquiries@watermeadowhouse.co.uk • www.watermeadowhouse.co.uk

Contact **Mrs P.M. Wallbridge,**
Watermeadow House,
Bridge Farm, Hooke,
Beaminster, Dorset DT8 3PD
Tel: 01308 862619

Superior Self-Catering Holiday Cottages

Six attractive and well equipped cottages on private estate in the centre of Dorset within easy reach of the coast. Heated indoor pool, gym, games room, tennis court, riding school, cycle hire. BBQ area, grounds, gardens, fenced ponds. Fishing, farm walks. Good central base for Heritage Coast and country.
Dogs by arrangement. Terms £290-£1055.

Luccombe Country Holidays

" Something for everyone at Luccombe"

Luccombe, Milton Abbas, Blandford Forum, Dorset DT11 OBE • Tel: 01258 880558
Fax: 01258 881384 • e-mail: mkayll@aol.com • www.luccombeholidays.co.uk

ETC
★★★★
SELF-CATERING

symbols

	Totally non-smoking		Pets Welcome
	Children Welcome	**SB**	Short Breaks
	Suitable for Disabled Guests		Licensed

Bournemouth, Burton Bradstock

Cardsmill Farm Holidays

**Whitchurch Canonicorum, Charmouth
Bridport, Dorset DT6 6RP**
Tel & Fax: 01297 489375 • e-mail: cardsmill@aol.com
www.farmhousedorset.com

Stay on a real working family farm in the Marshwood Vale, an Area of Outstanding Natural Beauty. Enjoy country walks to the village, coast and around farm and woods. Watch the daily milking, see baby calves and lambs, and seasonal activities here on this 590 acre farm. En suite family, double and twin rooms available, with CTV, tea/coffee trays. Also available, three large, rural, quiet farmhouses. Each has private garden, double glazed conservatory and ample parking. TAPHOUSE has 6 bedrooms, 4 bathrooms, lounge, 22'x15' kitchen/diner. COURTHOUSE COTTAGE and DAIRY each have 3 - 4 bedrooms and 2 or 3 bathrooms. Games room, parking, separate gardens. All have C/H, dishwasher, washing machine and very well equipped kitchen/diner/lounge. All available all year for long or short stays. Brochure available, or check the website. **B&B £25–£35pppn**

Immerse yourself in rural tranquillity. Set in an Area of Outstanding Natural Beauty, Wootton Fitzpaine nestles amidst rolling Dorset farmland. Within walking distance of the beaches and shops of Charmouth, world famous for its fossils, and three miles from the renowned Cobb at Lyme Regis. Golf, water sports and riding close by. We have four spacious, comfortable, well-furnished three-bedroomed cottages with open fires, inglenooks, heating and all amenities. Also large secluded, secure gardens with furniture, barbecues, parking.

www.westoverfarmcottages.co.uk

• Open all year • Pets and children welcome
• Logs and linen available • Guests are welcome to walk our farm • Terms from £190 to £795 per week, winter breaks available

**Jon Snook and Debby Snook,
Westover Farm Cottages,
Wootton Fitzpaine, Bridport DT6 6NE
01297 560451/561395
e-mail: wfcottages@aol.com**

WOOD DAIRY
WOOD LANE, NORTH PERROTT TA18 7TA

Three well-appointed stone holiday cottages set around courtyard in two and a half acres of Somerset/ Dorset countryside. Area of Outstanding Natural Beauty, close to Lyme Bay and Jurassic Coast. Excellent base for walking, trails and historic properties.

• Pets welcome by arrangement.
• Wheelchair friendly.
• All bookings will receive half price green fees.
• Direct access to Chedington Court Golf Club on the 8th and 9th greens.

**Tel & Fax: 01935 891532
e-mail: liz@acountryretreat.co.uk
www.acountryretreat.co.uk**

White Horse Farm ETC ★★★/★★★★

Self-Catering Barn Cottages

Set in beautiful Hardy countryside, we have five cottages furnished to high standards and surrounded by two acres of paddock and garden with a duck pond. We lie between the historic towns of Sherborne, Dorchester and Cerne Abbas. Within easy reach of many tourist attractions. Situated next door to an inn serving good food, we welcome pets. All cottages have central heating, colour digital TV and video recorder with unlimited free video-film rental. Electricity, bed linen, towels inclusive. Ample parking. Good value at £240 to £670 per week.

**The Willows sleeps 4/6; Toad Hall sleeps 4; Badger's sleeps 2; Ratty's sleeps 2/4; Moley's sleeps 2
White Horse Farm, Middlemarsh, Sherborne, Dorset DT9 5QN • 01963 210222**

Visit our website: www.whitehorsefarm.co.uk   e-mail: enquiries@whitehorsefarm.co.uk

Toller Porcorum, West Bay, Weymouth

Toller Porcorum is situated in picturesque rural Dorset, mid-way between the market towns of Dorchester and Bridport (20 minutes), and only six miles to West Bay and Heritage Coast.

The accommodation, a self-contained cottage with front and rear entrance, adjoins Barton Farmhouse at the end of the village High Street. Own driveway with ample parking for two cars and garden to both front and rear. Upstairs accommodation comprises one double and one single bedroom, and a modern bathroom, all fully carpeted. The downstairs is open-plan, with a spacious well-equipped modern kitchen/diner, which includes fridge, electric cooker and washing machine. The lounge is comfortably furnished, fully carpeted, with colour TV. Cloakroom and second toilet on the ground floor.

The Annexe

For bookings and enquiries contact: T.G. Billen, Barton Farmhouse, Toller Porcorum, Dorchester DT2 0DN
01300 320648

All linen supplied ♦ Pets by arrangement ♦ Terms: £150 – £200 per week, inclusive of electric heating and hot water ♦ Deposit required

This comfortably furnished bungalow, with attractive garden in a quiet cul-de-sac at West Bay, overlooks open field, only three minutes' walk to the harbour and beach. Ideal for family holidays, walking, fishing, visiting many places of interest or just relaxing.

Three bedrooms, two double and one twin bedded, sleeping six • Sitting room with colour TV • Well equipped kitchen/dining room. • Bathroom and separate toilet • Garden and parking space • Open all year • Out of season short breaks available • Personally supervised • Details from:

Robins
Meadway, West Bay, Bridport

Mrs B. Loosmore, Barlands, Lower Street, West Chinnock, Crewkerne, Somerset TA18 7PT
Tel: 01935 881790

SB

Grade II Listed Cottage with 3 bedrooms, 2 bathrooms, approx. one minute walk to beach, close to harbour.

VB ★★★

Other properties available weekly or short breaks.

Weymouth has a lovely sandy beach and picturesque harbour with pavement cafes. There is plenty to do all year round.

Phone: 01305 836495 • Mobile: 0797 1256160
e-mail: postmaster@buckwells.plus.com
www.holidaycottageweymouth.co.uk
www.holidaycottagesweymouth.co.uk

SB

Looking for holiday accommodation?
for details of hundreds of properties throughout the UK visit:

www.holidayguides.com

FREE or REDUCED RATE entry to Holiday Visits and Attractions – see our
READERS' OFFER VOUCHERS on pages 193-230

Broadwell

Gloucestershire

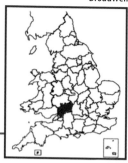

Gloucestershire, in an enviable position west of London between Bath, Oxford and Stratford-on-Avon, has style, elegance, charm.....and cheese rolling. The funkiest Farmers' Markets, happening hotels and, once a year, a mad scramble down the steepest slope to catch a cheese or two.

The county is best known for the Cotswolds, but the area includes The Royal Forest of Dean, Cheltenham, Tewkesbury and Gloucester.

In recent years the Cotswolds area has reinvented itself. Forget twee B&Bs and chintzy hotels, the Cotswolds is now a hotspot of chic hotels, award-winning designer farm shops and entertaining farmers' markets. Liz Hurley, Hugh Grant, Kate Moss, Kate Winslet and Sam Mendes have recently moved to the area and it's easy to see why. The Cotswolds offer space and escape in a beautiful environment and that's exactly what's on offer to visitors too.

Nearby, the Royal Forest of Dean is the last great English broadleaf forest, formerly a hunting ground for the kings of England. Nowadays it's emerging as a great destination for adrenaline sports and activity breaks, all against the backdrop of acres of woodland and nature reserves. It's one of the most colourful corners of England - daffodils, green shoots and bluebells in spring, and gold in Autumn.

The FHG Directory of Website Addresses
on pages 169-191 is a useful quick reference guide for
holiday accommodation with e-mail and/or website details

SB

WINCHCOMBE/TEWKESBURY. Orchard Cottage, Stanley Pontlarge, Near Winchcombe.
Set amid pear trees in orchard on Cotswold escarpment, three miles from Winchcombe. Rural privacy, own access and garden. Four people, ideally two adults and two children accommodated in two bedrooms; bathroom; sitting-diningroom (log-coal burning stove); night storage heaters; fully equipped; kitchen with electric cooker, etc. Linen provided. Car essential – parking. Shop three miles. Ideal centre for exploring, walking, sightseeing, all sports. Stratford-upon-Avon, Cheltenham, other interesting towns and villages within easy reach.
Rates: from £250 to £395 per week.
• Sleeps 4. • Pets by arrangement. • Children welcome.
• Open all year
ETC ★★★
Mrs S.M. Rolt, Stanley Pontlarge, Near Gretton, Winchcombe GL54 5HD (01242 602594).
e-mail: soniarolt@btinternet.com

Somerset

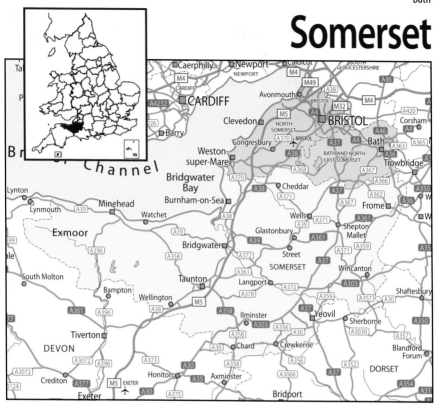

BATH. David & Jackie Bishop, Toghill House Farm, Freezing Hill, Wick, near Bath BS30 5RT (01225 891261; Fax 01225 892128).
Luxury barn conversions on working farm just north of Bath. Each cottage is equipped to a very high standard with bed linen provided. You are welcome to roam amongst our many animals and enjoy the outstanding country views. We also provide Bed and Breakfast accommodation in our warm and cosy 17th century farmhouuse where all rooms are en suite with TV and tea making facilities. .
• Pets welcome (£2 per night, £8 per week). • Children welcome.
• Non- smoking.
www.toghillhousefarm.co.uk

symbols

	Totally non-smoking		Pets Welcome
	Children Welcome	**SB**	Short Breaks
	Suitable for Disabled Guests		Licensed

symbols

	Totally non-smoking		Pets Welcome
	Children Welcome	SB	Short Breaks
	Suitable for Disabled Guests		Licensed

Langport, Minehead

MINEHEAD. 16th century thatched cottages.
All well equipped and attractively furnished, and situated within
ten minutes' walk of shops, sea and moor. Rose-Ash cottage
(sleeps 2) is all electric. Little Thatch (sleeps 5) has two double and
a single bedroom, and Willow Cottage (sleeps 6) has one double
and two twin bedrooms; both have gas central heating and
electric fires for chilly days. All have enclosed patio/garden and
private parking. Electricity and gas are metered; bed linen can be
provided at extra cost. Please send SAE for details.
• Sleep 2 - 6. • Pets welcome.
**Mr T. Stone, Troytes Farmstead, Tivington, Minehead
TA24 8SU (01643 704531).**

Publisher's note

While every effort is made to ensure accuracy, we regret that FHG Guides cannot accept
responsibility for errors, misrepresentations or omissions in our entries or any consequences
thereof. Prices in particular should be checked.
We will follow up complaints but cannot act as arbiters or agents for either party.

Wells, Weston-Super-Mare, Winscombe

SB

Wrinkle Mead

**Contact: Mrs C. Glass,
Islington Farm, Wells BA5 1US
Tel: 01749 673445**

Uniquely situated next to the Bishop's Palace, on the edge of the City of Wells (England's smallest city), Wrinkle Mead is a riverside stable conversion of the highest standard, completed in June 2004. In this tranquil setting, the cottage is surrounded by fields and parkland, and is part of Islington Farm, a smallholding of 2.5 acres. There is private parking. Just three minutes away is the ancient Market Place, leading to the High Street where there is a varied selection of shops, restaurants and eating places. Numerous golf courses, walking, riding, cycling and fishing are all available nearby.

SB

 SOMERSET COURT COTTAGES

Wick St Lawrence, Near Weston-super-Mare BS22 7YR • Tel: 01934 521383
Converted stone cottages in mediaeval village. 1, 2 or 3 beds.
Some with four-posters, luxury
whirlpool/spa baths. Superb centre
for touring West Country.
e-mail: peter@somersetcourtcottages.co.uk
www.somersetcourtcottages.co.uk

SB

HOME FARM COTTAGES

01934 842078
www.homefarmcottages.co.uk

Self-catering holiday cottages in an Area of Outstanding Natural Beauty. Home Farm Cottages consist of four beautifully converted stone outbuildings, all with original beams. All cottages are comfortable, warm and outstandingly well equipped, and guests have access to a hot tub in the gardens. The enclosed paddock is an ideal place for children to play in safety. It is a great place to relax and unwind, with many lovely walks in the area, and ideally situated for Cheddar, Wells, Longleat, Glastonbury and Bath. Sandy beaches are just five miles away. Local shops and pubs are within easy range.

**Mr C Sanders,
Home Farm
Cottages,
Barton,
Winscombe
BS25 1DX**

Publisher's note

While every effort is made to ensure accuracy, we regret that FHG Guides cannot accept responsibility for errors, misrepresentations or omissions in our entries or any consequences thereof. Prices in particular should be checked.
We will follow up complaints but cannot act as arbiters or agents for either party.

Chippenham, Devizes, Trowbridge

Wiltshire

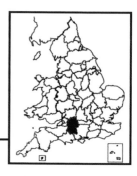

Dorney

Berkshire

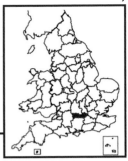

Buckinghamshire

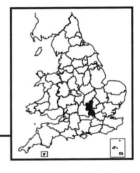

Buckingham

Hampshire

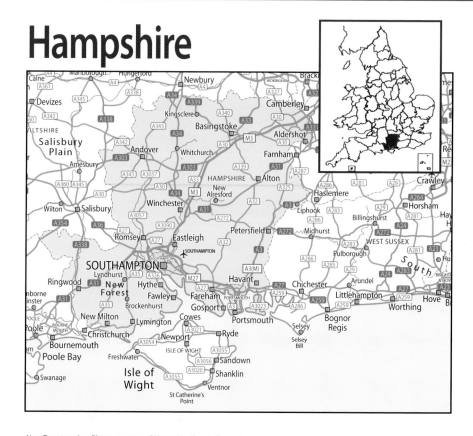

New Forest ponies. Picture courtesy of Hampshire County Council

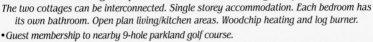

Bonchurch

Isle of Wight

The Isle of Wight has several award-winning beaches, including Blue Flag winners, all of which are managed and maintained to the highest standard. Sandown, Shanklin and Ryde offer all the traditional delights; or head for Compton Bay where surfers brave the waves, fossil hunters admire the casts of dinosaur footprints at low tide, kitesurfers leap and soar across the sea and paragliders hurl themselves off the cliffs

Newport is the commercial centre of the Island with many famous high street stores and plenty of places to eat and drink. Ryde has a lovely Victorian Arcade lined with shops selling books and antiques. Cowes is great for sailing garb and Godshill is a treasure chest for the craft enthusiast. Lovers of fine food will enjoy the weekly farmers' markets selling home-grown produce and also the Garlic Festival held annually in August.

Many attractions are out of doors to take advantage of the Island's milder than average temperatures. However, if it should rain, there's plenty to choose from. There are vineyards offering wine tasting, cinemas, theatres and nightclubs as well as sports and leisure centres, a bowling alley and an ice skating rink, home to the Island's very own ice hockey team – the Wight Raiders.

The Island's diverse terrain makes it an ideal landscape for walkers and cyclists of all ages and abilities. Pony trekking and beach rides are also popular holiday pursuits and the Island's superb golf courses, beautiful scenery and temperate climate combine to make it the perfect choice for a golfing break.

BONCHURCH. Ashcliff Holiday Apartment, Bonchurch PO38 1NT.
Idyllic and secluded position in the picturesque seaside village of Bonchurch. Self-contained, ground floor apartment adjoining Victorian house, set in large south-facing gardens with sea views and sheltered by a thickly wooded cliff. Large, private car park.
• Sleeps 2. • Dogs very welcome.
ETC ★★★
For free brochure telephone: 01983 853919.

FREE or REDUCED RATE entry to Holiday Visits and Attractions – see our
READERS' OFFER VOUCHERS on pages 193-230

Creek Gardens

Nestled in a tranquil setting overlooking the picturesque Wootton Creek. These high quality, well equipped holiday apartments and cottages are ideally located for all of the Isle of Wight's many attractions and sandy beaches.

Close to Cowes, host to sailing regattas every summer weekend, or for just enjoying a wealth of outdoor activities including walking, riding, cycling, fishing, exploring, or relaxing and soaking in the wonderful scenery.

**Creek Gardens, New Road, Ryde,
Isle of Wight PO33 4JX
Tel: 01983 883100
enquiries@creekgardens.co.uk**

www.creekgardens.co.uk

TOTLAND BAY. 3 Seaview Cottages, Broadway, Totland Bay.
This well-modernised cosy old coastguard cottage holds the Farm Holiday Guide Diploma for the highest standard of accommodation. It is warm and popular throughout the year. Located close to two beaches in beautiful walking country near mainland links. It comprises lounge/ dinette/kitchenette; two bedrooms (sleeping five); bathroom/toilet. Well furnished, fully heated, TV, selection of books and other considerations.
Rates: Four day winter break from £60; a week in summer £280.
• Sleeps 5. • Non-smokers only.
Mrs C. Pitts, 11 York Avenue, New Milton, Hampshire BH25 6BT (01425 615215).

Ventnor Holiday Villas

ETC ★★★

The apartments and villas are on a south-facing hillside leading down to a small rocky bay. The sea views are spectacular and the hillside sheltered, but open to all the sunshine that is going.

Villas sleep two to six, apartments sleep four.
Caravans also available, sleeping four.

Colour TV, no extra charge for linen. Free cots and high chairs. Car parking, sea view. Villas and caravans open April to October, apartments open all year. Three-night break per unit from £180. Pets welcome in villas. Write or phone for brochure.

**Mr King, Ventnor Holiday Villas, Wheelers Bay Road, Ventnor PO38 1HR
Tel: 01983 852973
e-mail: sales@ventnorholidayvillas.co.uk • www.ventnorholidayvillas.co.uk**

---

symbols

	Totally non-smoking		Pets Welcome
	Children Welcome	**SB**	Short Breaks
	Suitable for Disabled Guests		Licensed

St Margaret's Bay, Ware

Kent

Oxfordshire

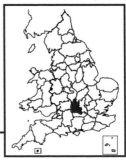

Battle

Sussex

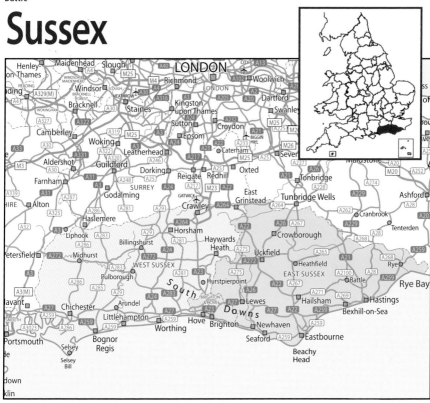

East Sussex

West Sussex

Ely

Cambridgeshire

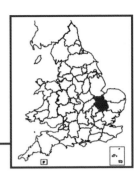

The Coach House has been imaginatively converted into a delightful abode full of character and charm, situated close to Ely Cathedral. Arranged on two floors, the accommodation downstairs comprises a sitting room and country-style kitchen. Upstairs there are two charming double rooms (one has a view of the Cathedral), and a cosy single room. All have an en suite bathroom, with a toilet, wash hand basin and a half-size bath with shower taps. Gas central heating. Linen, towels, toilet soap, cleaning materials and some basic provisions are provided.

SB

Prices range from £200 to £750 depending on season and length of stay. Special rates for two people.

Cathedral House, 17 St Mary's Street, Ely CB7 4ER • 01353 662124 e-mail: farndale@cathedralhouse.co.uk • www.cathedralhouse.co.uk

Hertfordshire

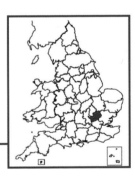

South Mimms

SOUTH MIMMS. Mr W.A.J. Marsterson, The Black Swan, 62/64 Blanche Lane, South Mimms, Potters Bar EN6 3PD (01707 644180; Fax: 01707 642344).
The Black Swan, a timber framed building dating from 1600, looks across the village green in South Mimms. Once a village inn, it is now our home. We have two flats and a cottage, convenient for M25 and A1(M), half-an-hour's drive, tube or train from central London. Near Junction 23 on M25. Follow signs to South Mimms village. Stay with us to see London and the South-East or use us as a staging post to or from the Channel Ports.
Rates: Self-catering from £210 to £300 per week.

• Sleep 2/6. • Children and pets welcome. • Non-smoking accommodation available.
ETC ★★/★★★

Bacton-on-Sea

Norfolk

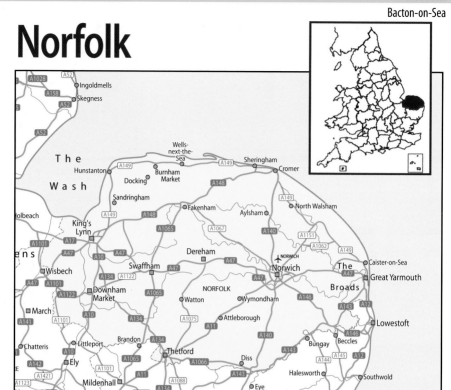

FHG Guides

publish a large range of well-known accommodation guides.

We will be happy to send you details or you can use the order form

at the back of this book.

East Dereham, Great Yarmouth, Hunstanton, Lyng

Terms quoted in this publication may be subject to increase if rises in costs necessitate

Sculthorpe, Thurne, Winterton-on-Sea, Worstead

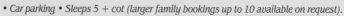

Suffolk

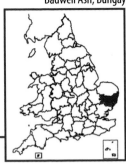

symbols

	Totally non-smoking	
	Children Welcome	
	Suitable for Disabled Guests	

Pets Welcome

SB Short Breaks

Licensed

•2 Forge Cottages • Friston • Suffolk

SB

Traditional Suffolk Cottage – the former Forge retaining some period features. Two minutes to pub, one mile to shops, Aldeburgh four miles. Sleeps 5. Secure garden, well equipped. All towels, linen provided. Short Breaks available. Open all year.

Contact: Debbie Pickering • Tel: 01621 810833
www.fristonholidaycottages.co.uk
e-mail: forgecottages2@btinternet.com

Kessingland Cottage Kessingland Beach

• Sleeps 6 • Children and disabled persons welcome • Available 1st March to 7th January •

An exciting three-bedroomed semi-detached cottage situated on the beach, three miles south of sandy beach at Lowestoft. Fully and attractively furnished with colour TV. Delightful sea and lawn views from floor-to-ceiling windows of lounge. Accommodation for up to six people. Well-equipped kitchen with electric cooker, fridge, hot and cold water; electric immersion heater. Electricity by £1 coin meter. Bathroom with bath and shower. No linen or towels provided. Only a few yards to beach and sea fishing. One mile to wildlife country park with mini-train. Buses quarter-of-a-mile and shopping centre half-a-mile. Parking, but car not essential.

SAE to Mr. S. Mahmood, 156 Bromley Road, Beckenham, Kent BR3 6PG (Tel & Fax: 020 8650 0539) e-mail: jeeptrek@kjti.co.uk • www.k-cottage.co.uk

Weekly terms from £95 in early March and early December to £375 in high season.

WINDMILL LODGES

Tel: 01728 685338 • Fax: 01728 684850
e-mail: holidays@windmilllodges.co.uk
www.windmilllodges.co.uk

SB

Our beautiful lodges are nestled around our small fishing lake in peaceful countryside. Each lodge features a secluded hot tub on the veranda - the perfect place to relax! Guests have use of indoor, heated swimming pool and fishing in private lake.

Individually furnished to a high standard, with dishwasher, cooker, fridge, microwave etc in the kitchen. Lounges feature large comfy sofas, TV, DVD, video and stereo. Full central-heating throughout. Veranda overlooking lake with barbecue and patio furniture.

Village pub within walking distance. Framlingham town with shops, restaurants and cafes only minutes away. Close to coast and attractions. Sleep 2 -8.

Windmill Lodges,
Red House Farm,
Saxtead, Woodbridge,
Suffolk IP13 9RD

Southwold • Walberswick

Furnished Holiday Cottages, Houses and Flats, available in this charming unspoilt Suffolk seaside town. Convenient for beaches, sailing, fishing, golf and tennis. Near to 300 acres of open Common. Attractive country walks and historic churches are to be found in this area, also the fine City of Norwich, the Festival Town of Aldeburgh and the Bird Sanctuary at Minsmere, all within easy driving distance. Brochure available on request.

**Durrants incorporating H.A. Adnams,
98 High Street, Southwold IP18 6DP
01502 723292 • Fax: 01502 724794
www.durrants.com**

Situated in small, picturesque village within 15 miles of Sudbury, Newmarket Racecourse and historic Bury St Edmunds.

Bungalow well equipped to accommodate 4 people.

All facilities • Car essential, parking. Children and pets welcome.

Terms from £71 to £141 per week • For further details send SAE to:

MRS M. WINCH, PLOUGH HOUSE, STANSFIELD, SUDBURY CO10 8LT • Tel: 01284 789253

Ashbourne

Derbyshire

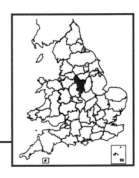

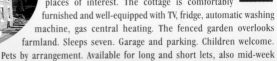

Herefordshire

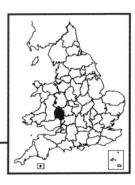

Herefordshire lies on the border with Wales, but is merely a stone's throw from Birmingham, Bristol, the Cotswolds and Cardiff. Green countryside, meandering rivers and acres of traditional cider orchards make up the landscape of this most rural of counties. It is home to the Hereford breed of cattle and has since become recognised for the standard of its local food and drink.

Hereford, a traditional Cathedral City but with the feel of a market town, offers visitors an interesting array of shops, cafes and bistros. The Norman Cathedral is home to the world famous Mappa Mundi, the oldest map of the world, and to the largest Chained Library in the world. The five market towns (Bromyard, Kington, Ledbury, Leominster and Ross-on-Wye) all offer something different to delight the visitor, and the 'Black and White Village' Trail explores a group of villages with beautiful half-timbered houses, cottages and country inns.

There is something for everyone – tranquil gardens, inviting tea-rooms, castles and historic houses, and of course, plenty of fresh country air in which to try canoeing, cycling, pony trekking, or maybe a good walk along one of the many long distance trails that intersect the county, including the recently opened Herefordshire Trail.

Rose Cottage is a modernised stone-built cottage (sleeps 5), retaining its original character situated at the foot of Black Mountains, on a quiet country road. Hay-on-Wye, Hereford and Abergavenny are easily accessible and the cottage is the ideal base for walking and touring. Many churches and castles of historic interest; close to River Monnow. Pony trekking, hang-gliding nearby. A car is essential and there is ample parking. Available all year round.

SB

Rose Cottage is comfortably furnished with full central heating and wood fire (heating and hot water included). Linen provided free of charge, towels available if required. Electricity by meter reading. Two bedrooms, one with double bed, one with three single beds (access through one bedroom into the other). Cot can be provided. Bathroom, toilet. Kitchen fully equipped with electric cooker, kettle, fridge, etc. Sittingroom; diningroom. TV. Dogs allowed. *Rates: from £190 to £210.*

Mrs M. Howard, The Three Horseshoes, Craswall, Hereford HR2 0PL • 01981 510631

The FHG Directory of Website Addresses

on pages 169-191 is a useful quick reference guide for
holiday accommodation with e-mail and/or website details

SB

Lincolnshire

Nottinghamshire

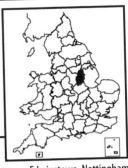

Edwinstowe, Nottingham

Shropshire

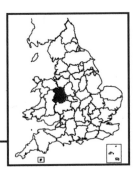

Shropshire is perhaps less well-known than other English counties. This is despite being the birthplace of Charles Darwin, home to the world's first iron bridge (now a World Heritage Site), having not one, but two of the finest medieval towns in England, inspiring the creation of the modern Olympics, and being the kingdom of the real King Arthur. After all, Shropshire is easy enough to find and get to from almost anywhere. (Hint: just north of Birmingham or south of Manchester depending on your direction of travel, and sitting snugly on the Welsh borders).

It may also come as a surprise to find out just how much is on offer. There are plenty of indoor and outdoor attractions, so the weather isn't a problem either. In Ironbridge, you can step into the past at the Ironbridge Gorge Museums where you'll find 10 museums to visit, all following the history of the Industrial Revolution. For retail therapy at its best, small independent shops can be found in all its market towns, full of those special 'somethings' you were looking for and even some things you weren't.

Shrewsbury is the beautiful county town, and home (naturally enough) to the Shrewsbury Summer Season – packed with over 200 events including the Shrewsbury Flower Show and the Cartoon Festival. There is also the Darwin Festival to celebrate the town's most famous son, and the foot-tapping Folk Festival. Ludlow, a medieval town, once the seat of the Welsh parliament, and now famed equally for its events and food, is also full of surprises. The Ludlow Festival is an annual two week gathering of actors, musicians, singers, entertainers, and generally some blooming interesting people to keep you rather amused.

All in all, Shropshire has a surprising amount to offer. So take the Shropshire option – for a great day out, fresh clean air and no jams (except those the W.I. make!)

symbols

 Totally non-smoking   Pets Welcome

 Children Welcome   SB Short Breaks

 Suitable for Disabled Guests   Licensed

Staffordshire

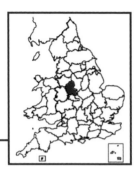

Situated in Staffordshire Moorlands, one cottage (sleeps 6) and one flat (sleeps 4), overlooking picturesque countryside. Fully equipped, comfortably furnished and carpeted throughout. Cottage, all on ground floor and with three bedrooms (one with four-poster) is suitable for the less able. An ideal base for visits to Alton Towers, the Potteries and Peak District. Patio, play area. Cot and high chair available. Laundry room with auto washer and dryer. Electricity and fresh linen inclusive. Terms from £180 to £350.

SB

EDITH & ALWYN MYCOCK,
'ROSEWOOD COTTAGE and ROSEWOOD FLAT',
LOWER BERKHAMSYTCH FARM, BOTTOM HOUSE,
NEAR LEEK ST13 7QP
Tel & Fax: 01538 308213
www.rosewoodcottage.co.uk

★★★
SELF CATERING

Warwickshire

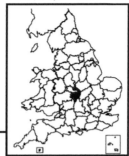

SB

Crimscote Downs Farm
Self-catering
Accommodation

PARADISE COTTAGE is a romantic hideaway for two people in a newly converted former shepherd's retreat, with views over the downs. It is full of character, and furnished and equipped to the highest standard.

THE DAIRY is ideal for a family visit, with fully equipped kitchen, sitting room and three en suite bedrooms. It has stunning views and is full of character with beams and wooden floors.

Terms from £210 to £425. Both cottages are fully centrally heated and only 5½ miles from Startford-upon-Avon. No smoking. Ample parking. Pets by arrangement.

Mrs J James, The Old Coach House, Whitchurch Farm, Wimpstone, Stratford-upon-Avon CV37 8PD (01789 450275).
e-mail: joan.james@tesco.net • www.stratford-upon-avon.co.uk/crimscote.htm

SB

COPES FLAT Brook Street, Warwick

Sleeps 3

Warwick town centre, secluded first floor flat dating from the mid 17th century, with its own entrance and high level garden, ideal for al fresco meals. The timber-framed sitting/dining room is comfortably furnished for eating and relaxing. Sorry, no pets. No smoking.

Colour TV • telephone • bathroom • bedroom with twin or double bed fully fitted kitchen • washing machine • tumble dryer

We are ideally situated for visiting Stratford-upon-Avon, Oxford, the Cotswolds and the main towns and attractions in the Heart of England.

Terms from £260-£360

Mrs Elizabeth Draisey, Forth House, 44 High Street, Warwick CV34 4AX
Tel: 01926 401512
e-mail: info@forthhouseuk.co.uk • www.forthhouseuk.co.uk

symbols

 Totally non-smoking

 Children Welcome

 Suitable for Disabled Guests

 Pets Welcome

SB Short Breaks

 Licensed

Worcestershire

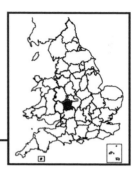

Greenbank Garden Flat, Malvern

This self-contained flat is situated in the Malvern Hills, overlooking Herefordshire. Quiet, cosy and convenient, it is an excellent base, fully equipped with gas hob, electric oven, microwave, fridge, TV, video, DVD, bath and shower, immersion heater, central heating throughout. Large conservatory and use of a garden. Sleeps 2-4 (double bed and double studio couch). Inclusive charge covers bed linen for the double bed, towels and all fuel. Children welcome. Country pub nearby; full services in Great Malvern (two miles). Short breaks available. Parking for car.

Rates: £150 to £230 weekly. Pets welcome by arrangement (£10 charge).

SB

Mr D.G. Matthews, Greenbank,
236 West Malvern Road, Malvern WR14 4BG
01684 567328 • e-mail: matthews.greenbank@virgin.net

Yorkshire

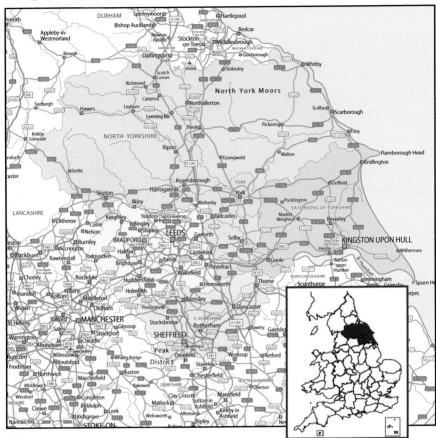

East Yorkshire

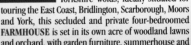
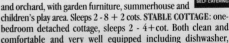

North Yorkshire

FREE or REDUCED RATE entry to Holiday Visits and Attractions – see our
READERS' OFFER VOUCHERS on pages 193-230

Fern Croft

**2 Mill Lane, Askrigg
Sleeps 4**

A modern cottage enjoying quiet location on edge of village with open fields rising immediately behind. Attractive and compact, this Wensleydale village is an ideal centre for the Dales, with facilities for everyday needs, including two shops, Post Office, restaurant and a couple of pubs. Furnished to a high standard for four, ground floor accommodation comprises large comfortable lounge/diner with colour TV and well-equipped kitchen. Upstairs there are two double bedrooms with a double and twin beds respectively, and modern bathroom. Storage heating included, other electricity by meter. Regret no pets. Terms from £160 to £290 weekly. Brochure:

Mr and Mrs K. Dobson • 01689 838450

THE GRANGE, Bishop Wilton, York YO42 1SA

Comfortably furnished cottages on working stud farm, within easy reach of York, Filey and Scarborough, Castle Howard, Yorkshire Moors National Park and the Steam Railway at Pickering. Accommodation, all ground floor, sleeps 2-4, plus cot, and comprises one double bedroom, open-plan sitting/diningroom with sofa bed, and kitchen. Well behaved pets. Covered parking. One cottage adapted for partially disabled guests. Small lawned area and BBQ. *From £160 to £350 per week,* including heat, power, linen and towels.

Judith Davy
Tel: 01759 369500 • Mobile: 07919 472456
www.thegrangefarm.com

★★★
SELF CATERING

Panoramic views, waterfalls, wild birds and tranquillity

Stone farmhouse with panoramic views, high in the Yorkshire Dales National Park (Herriot family's house in 'All Creatures Great and Small' on TV). Three bedrooms (sleeps 6-8), sitting and dining rooms with wood-burning stoves, kitchen, bathroom, WCs. House has electric storage heating, cooker, microwave, fridge, dishwasher, washing machine, colour TV, telephone. Garden, large barn, stables. Access from lane, private parking, no through traffic. Excellent walking from front door, near Wensleydale, Pets welcome. Self-catering from £400 per week.

Allaker in Coverdale,
West Scrafton, Leyburn, North Yorks DL8 4RM
For bookings telephone 020 8567 4862
e-mail: ac@adriancave.com • www.adriancave.com/allaker

Please note

All the information in this book is given in good faith in the belief that it is correct. However, the publishers cannot guarantee the facts given in these pages, neither are they responsible for changes in policy, ownership or terms that may take place after the date of going to press. Readers should always satisfy themselves that the facilities they require are available and that the terms, if quoted, still apply.

Grosmont, Hardraw, Harrogate, Helmsley

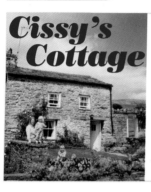

Low Bentham, Middlesmoor, Northallerton, Ripon

Durham

New Cottage, 'Law One',
Hollymoor Farm, Cockfield,
Bishop Auckland DL13 5HF
Telephone: 01388 718567/ 718260

NEW COTTAGE is a delightful little cottage in a very peaceful location.
The accommodation is very cosy and comfortable and all on one level – there are no stairs. Panoramic views from the lounge are a never-ending source of delight – they are stunning, and made even more beautiful in winter when there is a light dusting of snow. The cottage is accessible for country walks and sightseeing, and being able to start walks from the cottage is a real bonus.
And the sunsets are something else – truly magnificent.
Oil fired central heating is included in price.
Rates: £245 per week, all year round.
Details from Mrs Margaret Partridge.

SB

Bushblades Farm Cottage

Well equipped, comfortable farm cottage in rural setting with beamed ceilings and own private garden and patio. Ideal touring base. Close to Beamish Museum, Durham City, and MetroCentre. Northumberland coast can be reached in under an hour. 10 minutes from A1(M).

One well behaved dog welcome • Sleeps 2/3 (no children) • Terms from £200-£300
Short Breaks available in winter • For details contact Mrs Pamela Gibson

Bushblades Farm, Near Stanley, Co. Durham DH9 9UA • 01207 232722

symbols

	Totally non-smoking		Pets Welcome
	Children Welcome	**SB**	Short Breaks
	Suitable for Disabled Guests	♀	Licensed

Northumberland

Alnwick, Belford

WAREN LEA HALL

Waren Mill, Bamburgh

Luxurious Self-Catering
Holiday Accommodation
for families, parties and friends.

Near Bamburgh on the beautiful coast of Northumberland.

Standing on the shore of beautiful Budle Bay, an Area of Outstanding Natural Beauty and a Site of Special Scientific Interest for its birdlife, lies WAREN LEA HALL. This gracious Edwardian Gentleman's Residence, set in 2 ½ acres, enjoys spectacular views over the bay to Lindisfarne. In addition to the Hall there are two entirely self-contained apartments, GHILLIE'S VIEW and GARDEN COTTAGE.

THE HALL *(for up to 14 guests)*

Beautifully furnished to complement its Edwardian grandeur, with high ceilings, chandeliers, sash windows, fireplaces and polished wooden floors. Breathtaking views from every room. Large drawing and dining rooms opening on to floodlit terrace; large, fully equipped kitchen/breakfast room. Ground floor twin bedroom and cloakroom/shower room; upstairs five further family/twin/double rooms including en suite master with four-poster; family bathroom. Own garden and use of secluded, walled garden and parkland.

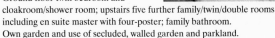

GARDEN COTTAGE *(for up to 4 guests)*

The terrace wing of Waren Lea Hall, reached through its own entrance from the garden. All the light and sunny rooms are prettily furnished with high quality fabrics, pine furniture and polished wooden floors throughout, and face the secluded garden which guests can use. The well equipped kitchen/dining room, double and twin bedrooms, one en suite, and family shower room are all on one level.

GHILLIE'S VIEW *(for up to 10 guests)*

The former home of the estate ghillie, accommodation is all on one level, with luxurious furnishings throughout. Fully equipped kitchen/dining room, semi-circular drawing room and master bedroom with four-poster and en suite shower; all with fine views across the river and bay to Holy Island. Double and twin rooms, one en suite, and family shower room Guests have use of walled garden and parkland.

For further information please contact the owners:

Carolynn and David Croisdale-Appleby

Abbotsholme, Hervines Road

Amersham, Buckinghamshire HP6 5HS

Tel: 01494 725194

Fax: 01494 725474 • Mobile: 07901 716136

E-mail: croisdaleappleby@aol.com

www.selfcateringluxury.co.uk

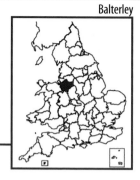

Balterley

Cheshire

Cheshire - soak in the atmosphere of the historic city of Chester, created by an abundance of black-and-white buildings set in a circuit of glorious city walls, the most complete in the country. Chester's crowning glory is the 13th century Rows – two tiers of shops running along the main streets, offering a unique and sophisticated shopping experience. A leisurely walk along the finest city walls in Britain will take you past most of the city's delights like the stunning Eastgate Clock and the 1000-year-old Cathedral, a haven of reflective tranquillity in a lively, bustling, cosmopolitan centre. The biggest archaeological dig in Britain is currently underway at the 2000-year-old Roman Amphitheatre; there is architectural splendour to enjoy at every turn. The lush countryside surrounding Chester is peppered with stately homes, award-winning gardens and chic market towns featuring characteristic black-and-white half-timbered buildings. Tatton Park near Knutsford is one of Britain's finest Georgian manors, with acres of parklands and formal gardens, a perfect attraction to enjoy in every season, and the host of the RHS Flower Show in July. Or visit Arley Hall and Gardens near Northwich, with its stunning herbaceous borders and Country Fair and Horse Trials in May. For super chic in super villages and towns, breeze into Tarporley, Nantwich, Knutsford and Wilmslow where sophisticated shopping, fine cuisine and contemporary pleasures ensure an afternoon of indulgence and fine delights, with food and drink festivals being held throughout the year.

Mrs Joanne Hollins,
Balterley Green Farm, Deans Lane,
Balterley, Near Crewe CW2 5QJ
Tel: 01270 820214

Jo and Pete Hollins offer guests a friendly welcome to their home on a 145-acre working farm in quiet and peaceful surroundings. Green Farm is situated on the Cheshire/Staffordshire border and is within easy reach of Junction 16 on the M6. An excellent stop-over place for travellers journeying between north and south of the country.

Two double en suite and two twin en suite in converted cottage can be either B&B or self-catering using the fully equipped kitchen in the cottage; all on ground floor. B&B from £25pp.
• Tea-making facilities and TV in all rooms • Cot provided
• Pets welcome • Open all year • Caravans and tents welcome
This area offers many attractions; we are within easy reach of historic Chester, Alton Towers and the famous Potteries of Staffordshire.

The FHG Directory of Website Addresses
on pages 169-191 is a useful quick reference guide for
holiday accommodation with e-mail and/or website details

Cumbria

Cumbria - The Lake District is often described as the most beautiful corner of England, and it's easy to see why 15 million visitors head here every year. It is a place of unrivalled beauty, with crystal clear lakes, bracken-covered mountains, peaceful forests, quiet country roads and miles of stunning coastline.

At the heart of Cumbria is the Lake District National Park. Each of the lakes that make up the area has its own charm and personality: Windermere, England's longest lake, is surrounded by rolling hills; Derwentwater and Ullswater are circled by craggy fells; England's deepest lake, Wastwater, is dominated by high mountains including the country's highest, Scafell Pike. For those who want to tackle the great outdoors, Cumbria offers everything from rock climbing to fell walking and from canoeing to horse riding – all among stunning scenery.

Cumbria has many delightful market towns, historic houses and beautiful gardens such as Holker Hall with its 25 acres of award-winning grounds. There are many opportunities to sample local produce, such as Cumbrian fell-bred lamb, Cumberland Sausage, and trout and salmon plucked fresh from nearby lakes and rivers.

Cumbria is a county of contrasts with a rich depth of cultural and historical interest in addition to stunning scenery. Compact and accessible, it can offer something for every taste.

When making enquiries please mention FHG GUIDES

**Stay Lakeland
35 Station Road
Cockermouth
Cumbria
CA13 9QW**

www.staylakeland.co.uk

A wide selection of quality inspected self-catering cottages, lodges and holiday caravans based in the Northern Lakes

CALL 0845 468 0936
9am – 5pm Mon to Sat

Ambleside

Ambleside, Bowness-on-Windermere, Broughton-in-Furness

THE EYRIE
Lake Road, Ambleside

SB

A really delightful, characterful flat nestling under the eaves of a converted school with lovely views of the fells, high above the village. Large airy living/diningroom with colour TV. Comfortably furnished as the owners' second home. Well equipped kitchen, spacious airing cupboard; three bedrooms sleeping six; attractive bathroom (bath/WC/shower) and lots of space for boots and walking gear. Fitted carpets, gas central heating, use of separate laundry room. Terrace patio with fine views. Sorry, but no pets. Available all year. Weekly rates £280 to £400. Also short breaks. Children welcome. Free parking permit provided for one car. Many recommendations. Brochure available.

Telephone Mrs Clark on:
01844 208208
e-mail: dot.clark@btopenworld.com

AMBLESIDE. 2 Lowfield, Old Lake Road, Ambleside.
Ground floor garden flat situated half a mile from town centre. The accommodation comprises lounge/dining room, kitchen, bathroom/WC, two bedrooms, one with en suite shower. Linen supplied. Parking for one car. Bookings run from Saturday to Saturday.
Rates: from £140 to £240 per week
• Sleeps 4. • Pets welcome. • Children welcome.
Mr P.F. Quarmby, 3 Lowfield, Old Lake Road, Ambleside LA22 0DH (Tel & Fax: 015394 32326).
e-mail: paulfquarmby@aol.com

43A Quarry Rigg, Bowness-on-Windermere

SB

Ideally situated in the centre of the village close to the Lake and all amenities, the flat is in a new development, fully self-contained, and furnished and equipped to a high standard for owner's own comfort and use. Lake views, ideal relaxation and touring centre. Close to Beatrix Potter Museum.
Accommodation is for two/three people. Bedroom with twin beds, lounge with TV, video and DVD; convertible settee; separate kitchen with electric cooker, microwave and fridge/freezer; bathroom with bath/shower and WC. Electric heating. Parking for residents.
Rates: Low season £180 to £230; High Season £230-£320
• *Weekends/Short Breaks also available.* • *Sleeps 2/3* • *Sorry, no pets.*
SAE, please, for details to E. Jones, 45 West Oakhill Park, Liverpool, Merseyside L13 4BN

Tel & Fax: 0151-228 5799
e-mail:
eejay@btinternet.com

Woodend Cottages
between the Eskdale and Duddon Valleys

Woodend is remote and surrounded by hills and moorland, with views towards Scafell Pike. The cottages and house offer cosy accommodation for two to six people.

Visit our website at www.woodendhouse.co.uk or phone 019467 23277

SHORT BREAKS AVAILABLE OUT OF SEASON

Readers are requested to mention this FHG
guidebook when seeking accommodation

Carlisle, Cartmel, Coniston, Dent

CARLISLE. Georgina and John Elwen, New Pallyards, Hethersgill, Carlisle CA6 6HZ (01228 577308).
Located approximately 12 miles north east of Carlisle, ideal for visiting Hadrian's Wall, The Lake District, Kielder Forest, Carlisle, Gretna Green and the Scottish Borders. New Pallyards is a small farm of 65 acres set in idyllic beautiful countryside, and our centrally heated cottages offer an excellent standard of accommodation with modern day facilities. Available with one to four bedrooms, all cottages are well equipped and heating and linen is provided (electricity metered). There is a large woodland beside the farm with a number of individual walks, also very close to golf courses, swimming pool, fishing and horse riding (usually available on the farm). Home cooked meals available in our farm guest house with residential licence. Please visit our website or contact us for further details.
Rates: from £150 to £672 per week depending on size of property.
ETC ★★★★
e-mail: newpallyards@btinternet.com
www.4starsc.co.uk

Seven cottages sleeping 2-6. Set behind a large Georgian house set in parkland on the side of Hamps Fell. Beautiful garden, great walks. Pets and children welcome. Open all year. Please telephone for details.

Contact: MR M. AINSCOUGH
LONGLANDS AT CARTMEL
CARTMEL LA11 6HG
Tel: 015395 36475
Fax: 015395 36172
e-mail: longlands@cartmel.com
www.cartmel.com

Ash Gill Cottages, *Torver, Near Coniston*

Set amidst the rolling hills surrounding Coniston Water, two adjoining houses both sleeping six and appointed to the highest standard. Central heating throughout for the cooler months. Bed linen and towels provided.

SB

Ample parking, gardens and patios. Excellent base for walking, touring, watersports and pony trekking.

Open all year for weeks and breaks.

Terms from £325 to £525 per week. Sorry, no pets.

Brochure and details from Mrs D. Cowburn, "Lyndene", Pope Lane, Whitestake, Near Preston, Lancashire PR4 4JR • 01772 612832

DENT VILLAGE

Character cottage for four
www.dentcottages.btinternet.co.uk
e-mail: dentcottages@btinternet.com

Tel: 015396 25294

Situated in the centre of the attractive old village of Dent with its narrow cobbled streets and surrounded by marvellous scenery. This delightful 17th century cottage is a Grade II Listed building and has been restored with care. The accommodation is comfortably furnished and is situated opposite Dent Church. This lovely holiday home enjoys an outlook over the surrounding countryside to the hills beyond and makes an ideal base for touring the Dales, or as a walking centre with open fells close at hand.

2 bedrooms - 1 double and 1 twin (with vanity unit), lounge with dining area, kitchen, and bathroom with toilet. Services: Electric fire in lounge, night storage heaters – all electricity included in the rent. Colour TV, shaver point, microwave oven. Large basement garage.

Grange-over-Sands, Grizedale Forest, Hartsop, Hawkshead

Ireby, Keswick

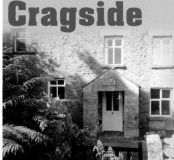

Kirkoswald, Lake District

KIRKOSWALD. Liz Webster, Howscales, Kirkoswald, Penrith CA10 1JG (01768 898666; Fax: 01768 898710). Howscales was originally a 17th century farm. The red sandstone buildings have been converted into five self-contained cottages, retaining many original features. Set around a cobbled courtyard, the cosy, well-equipped cottages for 2-4, are surrounded by award-winning gardens and open countryside. Shared laundry facilities. Cared for by resident owner. Ideal base from which to explore The Eden Valley, Lakes, Pennines and Hadrian's Wall. Please contact us or see our website for details.
Rates: £200 to £500 weekly.
• Sleeps 2/4. • Well-behaved pets welcome by arrangement.
• Non-smoking. • Open all year. • Short breaks available.
ETC ★★★★.
NATIONAL ACCESSIBILITY SCHEME: CATEGORY 2.
e-mail: liz@howscales.co.uk
www.howscales.co.uk

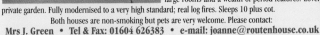

symbols

🚭	Totally non-smoking	🐕	Pets Welcome
🎠	Children Welcome	**SB**	Short Breaks
♿	Suitable for Disabled Guests	♉	Licensed

Lake District (Bowness/Hawkshead), Lamplugh, Millom, Newby Bridge, Penrith

Land Ends Cabins

Only one mile from Ullswater, our four detached log cabins have a peaceful fellside location in 25-acre grounds with two pretty lakes. Ducks, moorhens, red squirrels and wonderful birdlife. Doggy heaven! Sleep 2-5.

Land Ends Cabins
Watermillock, Near Ullswater CA11 0NB
Tel: 017684 86438
e-mail: infolandends@btinternet.com
www.landends.co.uk

FELL VIEW HOLIDAYS • FELL VIEW • GRISEDALE BRIDGE

Lovely, comfortable, well equipped accommodation in an idyllic location between Glenridding and Patterdale. Sleep 2-5. Magnificent views of the surrounding fells. Shared use of gardens.

Short Breaks available out of season.
Please look at the website or call for a brochure.

enquiries@fellviewholidays.com
www.fellviewholidays.com

GLENRIDDING, CUMBRIA CA11 0PJ • Tel: 017684 82795

A spacious well-equipped, comfortable cottage on a working farm. Superlative setting and views, large kitchen/dining room, Aga, lounge, open fire, TV/video/DVD, three bedrooms, bathroom, separate shower room. Linen, towels, electricity, logs and coal inclusive. Children and pets very welcome. Extensive garden. Storage heaters, washing machine, dishwasher. Easy reach Lake District, Scottish Borders and Roman Wall.

Sleeps 2-8 • Prices from £205–£455
Available all year.
Short breaks by arrangement.

FOXGLOVES COTTAGE. Mr & Mrs E. and J. Kerr,
Greenrigg Farm, Westward, Wigton CA7 8AH • 016973 42676

Quality Holiday Homes
in the beautiful Lake District

VisitBritain
★★★ –
★★★★★

LAKELOVERS
lakeland's self catering specialists

Quality Holiday Homes in England's Beautiful Lake District

Hundreds of VisitBritain inspected and graded properties throughout the southern and central Lake District. Lakelovers are sure to have a property to meet your needs. Free Leisure Club membership with every booking.

Tel: 015394 88855 • Fax: 015394 88857 • e-mail: bookings@lakelovers.co.uk • www.lakelovers.co.uk
Lakelovers, Belmont House, Lake Road, Bowness-on-Windermere, Cumbria LA23 3BJ
Low Fold Car Park, Lake Road, Ambleside, Cumbria LA22 0DN

Windermere

Langdale View Lodge, Windermere

Lovely log cabin with great views and sunsets from the veranda. Situated within White Cross Bay 5 star Leisure Park on the shores of Windermere. Excellent for exploring the Lake District and all outdoor pursuits. Facilities on site: Swimming pool, restaurant, shop, children's play area, tennis courts, boat launching available, sailing, woodland walks and more... Fully equipped for self-catering. Dog friendly. No agents fees.
Rates: from £385-£590 per week, Sat-Sat. Sleeps 5 max.
2 persons discount 20% off of out of season prices. Short breaks available.
See tariff on website. Pets welcome by arrangement. Parking for 2 cars.

SB

Contact: Jan Rhodes, The Croft, Gelt Road, Castle Carrock, Brampton, Cumbria CA8 9NE
Tel: 01228 670124 or mobile 07748 743 990 • e-mail: rhodes@rhodandjan.orangehome.co.uk

For full details of log cabin and local information visit www.lakeslogcabin.co.uk

Lancashire

Clitheroe, Morecambe

Rakefoot Farm
Chaigley, Near Clitheroe BB7 3LY
Tel: (Chipping) 01995 61332 or 07889 279063 • Fax: 01995 61296
e-mail: info@rakefootfarm.co.uk • website: www.rakefootfarm.co.uk

VisitBritain ★★★★
VisitBritain ★★★/★★★★

Family farm in the beautiful countryside of the Ribble Valley in the peaceful Forest of Bowland, with panoramic views. Ideally placed for touring Coast, Dales and Lakes. 9 miles M6 Junction 31a. Superb walks, golf and horse riding nearby, or visit pretty villages and factory shops. Warm welcome whether on holiday or business, refreshments on arrival.

BED AND BREAKFAST or SELF-CATERING in 17th century farmhouse and traditional stone barn conversion. Wood-burning stoves, central heating, exposed beams and stonework. Most bedrooms en suite, some ground floor. Excellent home cooked meals, pubs/restaurants nearby. Indoor games room, garden and patios. Dogs by arrangement. Laundry. **Past winner of NWTB Silver Award for Self-catering Holiday of the Year.**

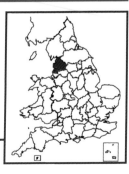

SB

B&B £25 - £32.50pppn sharing, £25 - £37.50pn single
S/C four properties (3 can be internally interlinked)
£105 - £649 per property per week. Short breaks available.

St Ives and Rydal Mount Holiday Flats
360-361 Marine Road, East Promenade,
Morecambe LA4 5AQ • 01524 411858

Situated on the sea front overlooking the bay and Lakeland hills. Ideal base for touring the Lake District and Yorkshire Dales. Large one or two bedroom flats occupying one floor, each with their own TV, electric cooker, fridge and microwave. Stair lift. Car park.
SAE please for brochure to Mrs S M Holmes

Channel Islands

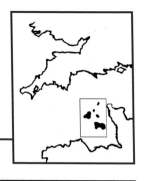

Other specialised holiday guides from FHG

Recommended **INNS & PUBS** OF BRITAIN

Recommended **COUNTRY HOTELS** OF BRITAIN

Recommended **SHORT BREAK HOLIDAYS** IN BRITAIN

The bestselling and original **PETS WELCOME!**

The **GOLF GUIDE,** *Where to Play, Where to Stay* IN BRITAIN & IRELAND

COAST & COUNTRY HOLIDAYS

BED & BREAKFAST STOPS

CARAVAN & CAMPING HOLIDAYS

CHILDREN WELCOME! Family Holiday & Days Out Guide

BRITAIN'S BEST LEISURE & RELAXATION GUIDE

Published annually: available in all good bookshops or direct from the publisher:

FHG Guides, Abbey Mill Business Centre, Seedhill, Paisley PA1 1TJ

Tel: 0141 887 0428 • Fax: 0141 889 7204

E-mail: admin@fhguides.co.uk • Web: www.holidayguides.com

Scotland

Scotland · Regions

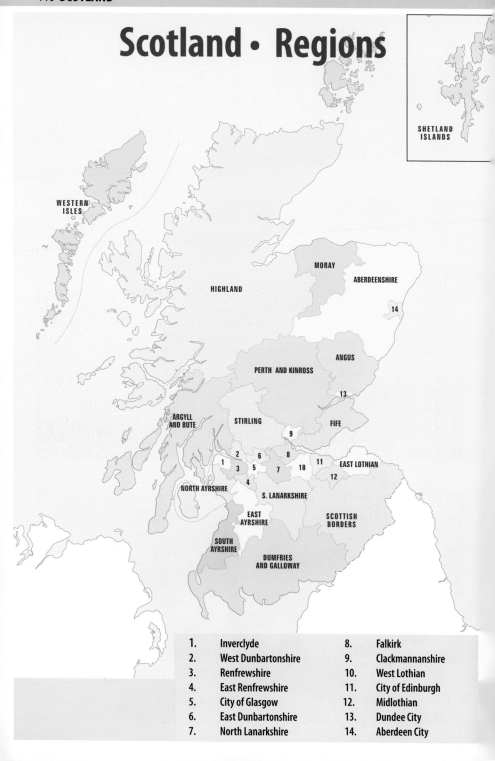

SHETLAND
ISLANDS

WESTERN
ISLES

MORAY

ABERDEENSHIRE

HIGHLAND

14

ANGUS

PERTH AND KINROSS

13

ARGYLL
AND BUTE

STIRLING

FIFE

9

2
6
8
1
11
3
5
7
10
EAST LOTHIAN
4
12

NORTH AYRSHIRE

S. LANARKSHIRE

EAST
AYRSHIRE

SCOTTISH
BORDERS

SOUTH
AYRSHIRE

DUMFRIES
AND GALLOWAY

1.	Inverclyde	8.	Falkirk
2.	West Dunbartonshire	9.	Clackmannanshire
3.	Renfrewshire	10.	West Lothian
4.	East Renfrewshire	11.	City of Edinburgh
5.	City of Glasgow	12.	Midlothian
6.	East Dunbartonshire	13.	Dundee City
7.	North Lanarkshire	14.	Aberdeen City

Dunnottar Castle, Aberdeenshire. Picture courtesy of Aberdeen and Grampian Tourist Board

FREE or REDUCED RATE entry to Holiday Visits and Attractions – see our
READERS' OFFER VOUCHERS on pages 193-230

Banchory

Aberdeenshire, Banff & Moray

Aberdeenshire, Banff & Moray - one of the easiest ways to explore the area is by following one of the signposted tourist routes and theme trails. Perhaps the most famous of these is the Malt Whisky Trail around magnificent Speyside which links the award winning Speyside Cooperage and eight famous distilleries. Aberdeenshire is very much Scotland's "Castle Country" and 13 of the region's finest castles and great houses are located along Scotland's only Castle Trail. A lesser known feature of Scotland's North East is the fact that 10% of Scotland's Standing Stones are to be found here. Archaeolink, Scotland's prehistory park, interprets the early history of Grampian and promotes a journey through time for all ages. Royal Deeside has many attractions associated with Queen Victoria and a succession of British monarchs. There are many well known sites in this part of the region along the Victorian Heritage Trail including Balmoral Castle, home to royalty for 150 years, Crathie Church, Royal Lochnagar Distillery and Loch Muick. Around the Coastal Trail you will find some of Europe's best coastline, visually stunning, clean air and clear seawater. There are delightful villages such as the "Local Hero" village of Pennan, picturesque harbours, spectacular cliff formations, 150 miles of unspoilt beaches and fabulous golf courses such as Cruden Bay, Royal Tarlair, Duff House Royal and many more along the Moray Firth, as well as the company of the area's wildlife from dolphins to seals and seabirds.

symbols

Totally non-smoking		Pets Welcome	
Children Welcome		**SB** Short Breaks	
Suitable for Disabled Guests		Licensed	

Argyll & Bute

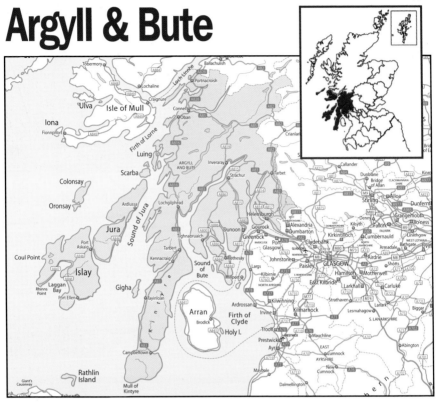

FHG Guides

publish a large range of well-known accommodation guides.

We will be happy to send you details or you can use the order form

at the back of this book.

ROSNEATH CASTLE PARK

SO NEAR... YET SO FAR AWAY

Rosneath Castle Park has everything to offer if you are looking for a touring or camping holiday. No more than an hour's drive from Glasgow, the 57 acres that the park occupies along the shore of Gareloch offer the perfect opportunity to relax and discover another world, and another you.

Thistle Awarded Luxury Self-Catering Holiday Homes with superb views. In a beautiful setting with first class facilities including an adventure playground, boat house, fun club, restaurant and bar, there's no end to the reasons why you would 'wish you were here'.

**Rosneath Castle Park, Rosneath,
Near Helensburgh, Argyll G84 0QS
Tel: (01436) 831208
Fax: (01436) 831978
enquiries@rosneathcastle.demon.co.uk
www.rosneathcastle.demon.co.uk**

COLOGIN – a haven in the hills

If you've just got married or just retired, have toddlers in tow or dogs you can't bear to leave at home, or you just want to get away for a break with all the freedom of a self-catering holiday, then we may have just what you are looking for. Our cosy chalets and well appointed lodges offer everything you need for a relaxing country holiday.

One of the most appealing features of Cologin is its peace and tranquillity. With 14 lodges, 4 chalets, Cologin Farmhouse and Cruachan Cottage at Cologin we have plenty of different accommodation options. Choose from a cosy one-bedroom chalet or the larger two-bedroomed lodges, or sleep up to 10 adults and 4 children in our traditional Scottish farmhouse.

Our award-winning family-friendly pub and restaurant, **The Barn,** is within easy reach of all our properties. It's a perfect place to unwind and relax. With its unique atmosphere and friendly staff it is the reason why many of Cologin's guests return year after year.

If you love the great outdoors come rain or shine and want to escape from the routine of city life, Cologin is for you. With 17,000 acres of waymarked forest trails above the farm you can enjoy nature at its finest, with glorious scenery and breathtaking views from the summit over Oban Bay to the islands beyond.

Contact us for colour brochure:
Jim and Linda Battison – resident owners
Cologin, Lerags Glen, Oban, Argyll PA34 4SE
Telephone: 01631 564501 • Fax: 01631 566925
e-mail: info@cologin.co.uk
www.cologin.co.uk

COLOGIN
a haven in the hills
STB ★★★–★★★★
Self Catering

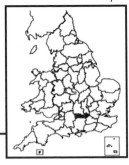

Ayrshire & Arran

Ayrshire and Arran has always held a special affinity with families and this is reflected in the many fun attractions and activities geared towards children. These include farm parks, theme parks with daring funfair rides, and many sports and leisure centres. There's plenty to see and do with features like the Vikingar Viking Centre at Largs and The Scottish Industrial Railway Centre at Dalmellington adding to established attractions like Culzean Castle and the thriving business built on the life, loves and works of Scotland's best-loved poet, Robert Burns. A visit to the Secret Forest at Kelburn Country Centre is a must – its canopy of trees hides a multitude of surprises, the green man, the spirit of the forest, a Chinese garden with pagoda, and a crocodile swamp. Older visitors may enjoy a visit to Ayr Racecourse, enjoy a shopping spree, or treat themselves to a round on one the area's 44 golf courses. Whether the pace is leisurely or frantic, it's got to be Ayrshire and the Isle of Arran.

Please note

All the information in this book is given in good faith in the belief that it is correct. However, the publishers cannot guarantee the facts given in these pages, neither are they responsible for changes in policy, ownership or terms that may take place after the date of going to press. Readers should always satisfy themselves that the facilities they require are available and that the terms, if quoted, still apply.

Borders

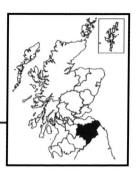

THE SCOTTISH BORDERS stretch from the rolling hills and moorland in the west, through gentler valleys to the rich agricultural plains of the east, and the rocky Berwickshire coastline with its secluded coves and picturesque fishing villages. Through the centre, tracing a silvery course from the hills to the sea, runs the River Tweed which provides some of the best fishing in Scotland. As well as fishing there is golf – 18 courses in all, riding or cycling and some of the best modern sports centres and swimming pools in the country. Friendly towns and charming villages are there to be discovered, while castles, abbeys, stately homes and museums illustrate the exciting and often bloody history of the area. It's this history which is commemorated in the Common Ridings and other local festivals, creating a colourful pageant much enjoyed by visitors and native Borderers alike.

One of the delights of travelling is finding gifts and keepsakes with a genuine local flavour, and dedicated souvenir hunters will find a plentiful supply of traditional delicacies, from drinks to baking and handmade sweets. Handcrafted jewellery, pottery, glass and woodwork, as well as beautiful tweeds and high quality knitwear can be found in the many interesting little shops throughout the area.

Scottish Borders eating establishments take pride in providing particularly good food and service and the choice of hotels, inns restaurants and cafes make eating out a real pleasure.

Details from:
Mrs Sheila Letham, Fireburn Mill,
Coldstream TD12 4LN
01890 882124 • Fax: 01890 883838
andrewletham@tiscali.co.uk

'Meg's' and 'Nellie's' Cottages. These comfortable and homely semi-detached cottages, situated on a private road, have lovely views across the River Tweed and rolling Border country to the Cheviot Hills. They are heated throughout, and in winter the sittingrooms have a welcoming open fire. Both have a sittingroom, kitchen, bathroom and double bedroom on the ground floor. 'Meg's' has one twin and one family room on the first floor. 'Nellie's' has two twin rooms. Full linen included. Both have colour TV/DVD, fridge, washing machine and garden furniture. Cot and high chair can be provided. Ample parking. Dogs by prior arrangement.
Short Breaks available • Terms from £120

Fishing on the River Tweed is just a short walk from the cottages. One complimentary permit for trout fishing is available for each cottage.

The 18-hole Hirsel golf course is only one mile from the cottages and a number of other courses for you to enjoy are nearby.

Signposted riverside and woodland walks are adjacent and a short drive will take you to hill walks in the Cheviots and Lammermuirs, including the northern end of the Pennine Way and eastern end of the Southern Upland Way.

SB

The FHG Directory of Website Addresses
on pages 169-191 is a useful quick reference guide for holiday accommodation with e-mail and/or website details

Dumfries & Galloway

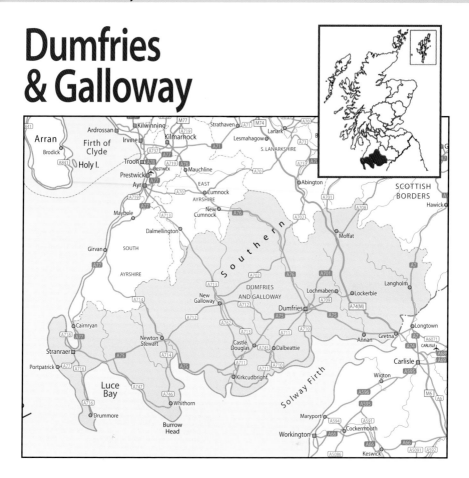

DUMFRIES & GALLOWAY is a mixture of high moorland and sheltered glens, and presents abundant opportunities for hill walking, rambling, fishing for salmon and sea trout, cycling, bird watching and field sports. There are at least 32 golf courses, ranging from the challenging Stranraer course at Creachmore to the scenic, clifftop course at Port Patrick. The Stranraer course has the distinction of being the last course designed by James Braid. The warming influence of the Gulf Stream ensures a mild climate which makes touring a pleasure, and many visitors come here to visit the dozens of interesting castles, gardens, museums and historic sites. In addition, pony trekking and riding plus a never-ending succession of ceilidhs, village fairs, country dances, classical music concerts and children's entertainment guarantee plenty of scope for enjoyment. Discover the many hidden secrets of this lovely and unspoilt landscape such as the pretty little villages along the coast or visit some of the interesting towns in the area including Stranraer, the principal town and ferry port with its busy shopping streets, park and leisure centre. Those who love 'the written word' must surely visit the book town of Wigtown, and the gourmet amongst us will love the new concept of Castle Douglas, the recently designated 'Food Town'.

CASTLE DOUGLAS. Cala-Sona, Auchencairn, Castle Douglas.
A stone-built house in centre of Auchencairn village, near shops, Post Office and garage. To let, furnished. Linen supplied. Two bedrooms (one double bed; two single beds); cot available. Bathroom, bedroom with double bed, livingroom and kitchenette with electric cooker, fridge and geyser. Auchencairn is a friendly seaside village and you can enjoy a peaceful holiday here on the Solway Firth where the Galloway Hills slope down to the sea. Many places of historic interest to visit, also cliffs, caves and sandy beaches. A haven for ornithologists. SAE brings prompt reply. Car essential - parking.
• Sleeps 6.
Mrs Mary Gordon, 7 Church Road, Auchencairn, Castle Douglas DG7 1QS (01556 640345).

---

barncrosh farm

Self-catering farm holiday cottages in South West Scotland

SB

Whatever your interests, from family groups relaxing on holiday together, to outdoor enthusiasts relishing out-of-season activities, you will find so much to enjoy in the peaceful surroundings of Barncrosh, on our farm in the heart of Dumfries & Galloway. We offer a wide choice of self-catering holiday accommodation, sleeping from 2 people right up to 12. Many are ideal for disabled holidays.

Tennis court, adventure playground and indoor games room. Shops, pubs and restaurants in Castle Douglas (4 miles) and Kirkcudbright (5 miles).

Barncrosh, Castle Douglas, Kirkcudbrightshire, DG7 1TX
Telephone: 01556 680 216 • Fax: 01556 680 442
e-mail: enquiries@barncrosh.co.uk • www.barncrosh.co.uk

BAREND HOLIDAY VILLAGE — SANDYHILLS, DALBEATTIE DG5 4NU

Escape to the beautiful South West Colvend coast, the perfect base for walking, touring and cycling in Dumfries & Galloway, which is Scotland in miniature, and only one hour's drive from England.

SB

Our chalets, situated only a short walk from Sandyhills beach, are well equipped and centrally heated for all year comfort. Pets welcome or pet-free. Their decks overlook our loch or Colvend 18-hole golf course, and the surrounding countryside teems with wildlife - red squirrels, badgers and deer are our neighbours.

On-site boules courts, bar, restaurant, sauna and indoor pool.

3 days minimum: any day of entry, prices include linen and swimming. From £255 for four for 3 days.

Tel: 01387 780663
e-mail: fhg@barendholidayvillage.co.uk
www.barendholidayvillage.co.uk

Barend
HOLIDAY VILLAGE

No. 4 Silver Birches Close
Dalbeattie DG5 4UQ
Tel: 01556 502108
07808 964 875

SB

Situated off the Solway Coast Road in the granite town of Dalbeattie, adjacent to the forest for walking and mountain biking. Furnished to a high standard, offering a very warm welcome at

any time of the year. Beach seven miles away. Golf, horse riding and river fishing (by permit) are available nearby. Visit the 'food town' of Castle Douglas or the 'artists' town' of Kirkcudbright, the varied coast and the lovely rolling Galloway Hills. Secure storage for bicycles in garage. Well behaved dogs welcome (bring own bedding).

Let Friday to Friday • e-mail: kathrynkd@btinternet.com

A useful index of towns/counties appears on pages 233-236

Dunbartonshire

symbols

	Totally non-smoking		Pets Welcome
	Children Welcome	**SB**	Short Breaks
	Suitable for Disabled Guests		Licensed

Fife

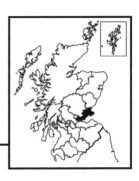

Fife - whether as 'County', 'Region' or more traditionally 'Kingdom', Fife has always been a prosperous and self-contained part of Scotland. The coast, with small ports such as Crail, Anstruther, Pittenweem, St Monance, Elie and the more commercial Methil, Burntisland and Kirkcaldy, has always been interesting and important. St Andrews with its university, castle, cathedral and golf, is the best known and most visited town. Dunfermline has a historic past with many royal associations and was the birthplace of the philanthropist, Andrew Carnegie. Medieval buildings have been restored by the National Trust in nearby Culross. Cupar, Falkland, Kinross (for Loch Leven), Auchtermuchty and Leuchars are amongst the many other historic sites in Fife, and at North Queensferry is one of Fife's newest and most popular attractions, Deep Sea World. The picturesque seaside village of Aberdour with its own castle is nearby.

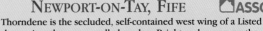

Glasgow & District

Glasgow & District -in one of Europe's most dynamic cultural centres, there's so much to see and do – from the City of Glasgow itself, alive with heritage, entertainment and nightlife, to the charm of the bustling towns, scenic villages and countryside of the surrounding districts. Entertainment and sport feature in an exciting year-round calendar that encompasses opera and theatre, Scottish ceilidhs and top sporting events. Glasgow is home to a multitude of shops, from boutiques and specialist stores to High Street favourites and shopping malls, such as Buchanan Galleries and Princes Square. The city is brimming over with restaurants, cafes, bars and bistros. Culinary treats include many Scottish dishes, plus a wide range of international cuisine, with prices to suit every pocket. The famous River Clyde links city life to country life as it flows from its source in the Lowther Hills to the maritime towns and villages of Inverclyde and Renfrewshire.

The Garden Flat

SB

Studio-style ground floor flat at the rear of our family home; own private entrance. One double bedroom, living room with fold-out bed, fully equipped kitchen, bathroom. No hidden extras – all linen, heating and light included in price. Small private garden at rear with garden furniture and drying area. Motorway network nearby; ideal touring base; rail & bus service to Glasgow, 5.5 miles.
From £220 to £300 per week. Triple occupancy - price on application.
• No pets • Children welcome • Non-smoking only
• Open all year • B&B also available
Mrs P. Wells • *0141-779 1990* • *Fax: 0141-779 1951*
e-mail: phyl@avenueend.co.uk • *www.avenueend.co.uk*

"Avenue End"
21 West Avenue, Stepps,
Glasgow G33 6ES

Visit the FHG website
www.holidayguides.com
for details of the wide choice of accommodation
featured in the full range of FHG titles

Highlands

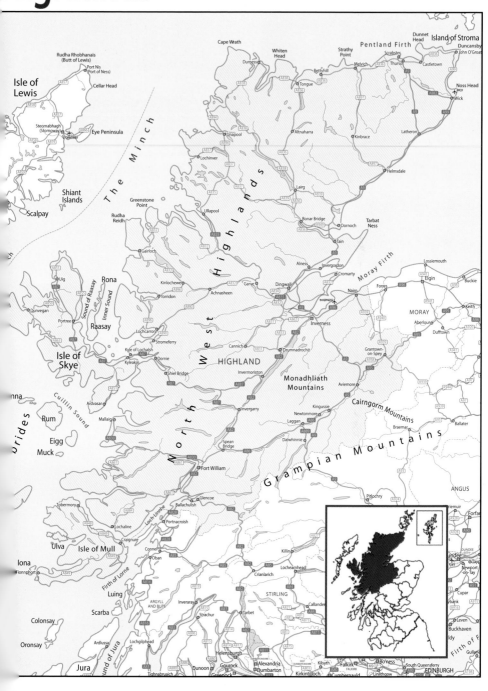

SPEYSIDE LEISURE PARK

SB

*Self-Catering
Holidays
in the Heart
of the
Highlands*

The park is situated in a quiet riverside setting with mountain views, only a short walk from Aviemore centre and shops. We offer a range of warm, well equipped chalets, cabins and caravans, including a caravan for the disabled. Prices include electricity, gas, linen, towels and use of our heated indoor pool and sauna. There are swings, a climbing frame and low level balance beams for the children. Permit fishing is available on the river. Discounts are given on some local attractions.

Families, couples or groups will find this an ideal location for a wide range of activities including:

* *Horse riding* • *Golf* • *Fishing* • *Hillwalking*
* *RSPB Reserves* • *Mountain and Watersports* • *Reindeer herd*
* *Steam railway and the Whisky Trail*

Only slightly further afield you will find Culloden Moor, the Moray Firth dolphins and of course, the not to be missed, Loch Ness.
Accommodation sleeps from 4–8, but we offer a reduced rate for a couple.
Short Breaks are available. Sorry, no pets, except guide and hearing dogs.

Speyside Leisure Park
Dalfaber Road, Aviemore, Inverness-shire PH22 1PX
Tel: 01479 810236 • Fax: 01479 811688
e-mail: fhg@speysideleisure.com • www.speysideleisure.com

Boat of Garten, Brora, Drumnadrochit

Lochcarron, Newtonmore, Poolewe, Spean Bridge

LOCHCARRON. The Cottage, Stromecarronach, Lochcarron West, Strathcarron.
The small, stone-built Highland cottage is fully equipped and has a double bedroom, shower room and open plan kitchen/living room (with open fire). It is secluded, with panoramic views over Loch Carron and the mountains. River, sea and loch fishing are available. Hill-walking is popular in the area and there is a small local golf course. Nearby attractions include the Isle of Skye, Inverewe Gardens, the Torridon and Applecross Hills and the historic Kyle Railway Line. For full particulars write, or telephone.
SB
• Working croft. • Sleeps 2. • Dogs welcome, under control at all times.
Mrs A.G. Mackenzie, Stromecarronach, Lochcarron West, Strathcarron IV54 8YH (01520 722284). www.lochcarron.org

A useful index of towns/counties appears on pages 233-236

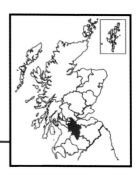
Lanarkshire

Biggar (Clyde Valley)

symbols

 Totally non-smoking

 Children Welcome

 Suitable for Disabled Guests

 Pets Welcome

SB Short Breaks

 Licensed

Perth & Kinross

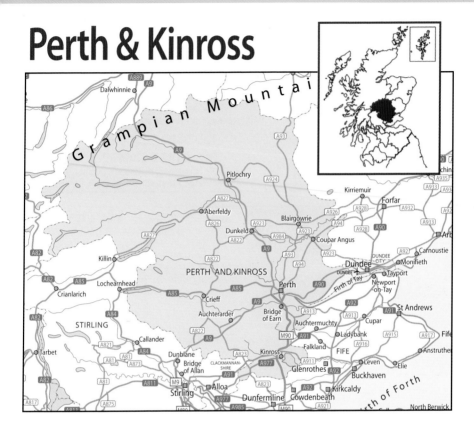

Perth & Kinross embraces both Highland and Lowland. Close to where the two Scotlands meet, a cluster of little resort towns has grown up: Crieff, Comrie, Dunkeld, Aberfeldy, and Pitlochry, set, some say, right in the very centre of Scotland. Perthshire touring is a special delight, as north-south hill roads drop into long loch-filled glens - Loch Rannoch, Loch Tay or Loch Earn, for example. No matter where you base yourself, from Kinross by Loch Leven to the south to Blairgowrie by the berryfields on the edge of Strathmore, you can be sure to find a string of interesting places to visit. If your tastes run to nature wild, rather than tamed in gardens, then Perthshire offers not only the delights of Caledonian pinewoods by Rannoch and the alpine flowers of the Lawers range, but also wildlife spectacle such as nesting ospreys at Loch of the Lowes by Dunkeld. There are viewing facilities by way of hides and telescopes by the lochside. Water is an important element in the Perthshire landscape, and it also plays a part in the activities choice. Angling and sailing are two of the 'mainstream' activities on offer, though if you are looking for a new experience, then canyoning is a Perthshire speciality on offer from a number of activity operators. Enjoy a round of golf on any of Perthshire's 40 courses, including those at Gleneagles by Auchterarder.

The main town of Perth has plenty of shops with High Street names as well as specialist outlets selling everything from Scottish crafts to local pearls. With attractions including an excellent repertory theatre and a great choice of eating places, this is an ideal base to explore the true heartland of Scotland.

Stirling & The Trossachs

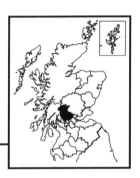

At the heart of Scotland, **STIRLINGSHIRE** has played a central role in most aspects of the nation's life. History and geography have converged here in road and rail routes, in decisive sieges and battles, in important industrial developments and heritage. The county enjoys the natural riches of the Forth valley and the economic wealth of Grangemouth and Falkirk. The town of Stirling itself is a natural tourist centre, both for its own attractions, such as the historic castle and the excellent shopping facilities, and as a base for other visitor attractions close at hand. Villages and small towns such as Drymen, Killearn, Fintry and Kippen offer hospitality and interesting outings. Loch Lomond and The Trossachs National Park is less than an hour from Glasgow, yet feels worlds apart from the bustle of city life. Explore wild glens and sparkling lochs, and for the more energetic, low-level walking, cycling, hill walking, and the new sport of canyoning can be enjoyed.

Scottish Islands

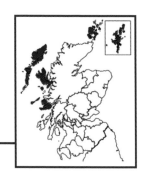

Isle of Lewis

Carloway, Lewis

SB

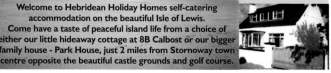
The FHG Directory of Website Addresses
on pages 169-191 is a useful quick reference guide for holiday accommodation with e-mail and/or website details

North Uist

Clachan Sands

Orkney Islands

Orkney - Less than 10 miles from the Scottish mainland across the Pentland Firth, the 70-odd islands of Orkney are rich in pre-history, but thinly populated in present times. Kirkwall, the capital, is on Mainland, the largest island, where the most accessible and best-known ancient sites are found, inlcuding Maes Howe and Skara Brae. The ruins of Notland Castle on the northern island of Westray, and the famous sheltered harbour of Scapa Flow are other Orkney landmarks.

Kirkwall

Looking for Holiday Accommodation?

for details of hundreds of properties throughout the UK, visit our website
www.holidayguides.com

Wales

Ratings & Awards

For the first time ever the AA, VisitBritain, VisitScotland, and the Wales Tourist Board will use a single method of assessing and rating serviced accommodation. Irrespective of which organisation inspects an establishment the rating awarded will be the same, using a common set of standards, giving a clear guide of what to expect. The RAC is no longer operating an Hotel inspection and accreditation business.

Accommodation Standards: Star Grading Scheme

Using a scale of 1-5 stars the objective quality ratings give a clear indication of accommodation standard, cleanliness, ambience, hospitality, service and food, This shows the full range of standards suitable for every budget and preference, and allows visitors to distinguish between the quality of accommodation and facilities on offer in different establishments. All types of board and self-catering accommodation are covered, including hotels, B&Bs, holiday parks, campus accommodation, hostels, caravans and camping, and boats.

VisitBritain and the regional tourist boards, enjoyEngland.com, VisitScotland and VisitWales, and the AA have full details of the grading system on their websites

The more stars, the higher level of quality

★★★★★
exceptional quality, with a degree of luxury

★★★★
excellent standard throughout

★★★
very good level of quality and comfort

★★
good quality, well presented and well run

★
acceptable quality; simple, practical, no frills

National Accessible Scheme

If you have particular mobility, visual or hearing needs, look out for the National Accessible Scheme. You can be confident of finding accommodation or attractions that meet your needs by looking for the following symbols.

 Typically suitable for a person with sufficient mobility to climb a flight of steps but would benefit from fixtures and fittings to aid balance

 Typically suitable for a person with restricted walking ability and for those that may need to use a wheelchair some of the time and can negotiate a maximum of three steps

 Typically suitable for a person who depends on the use of a wheelchair and transfers unaided to and from the wheelchair in a seated position. This person may be an independent traveller

 Typically suitable for a person who depends on the use of a wheelchair in a seated position. This person also requires personal or mechanical assistance (eg carer, hoist).

Anglesey & Gwynedd

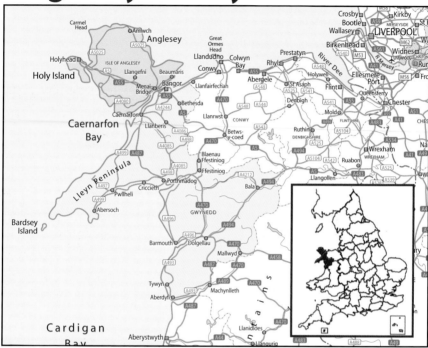

ANGLESEY & GWYNEDD, the northernmost area of Wales, bordered by the Irish sea, has something for everyone. Its beautiful coastline has glorious sandy beaches which offer safe bathing, and there are quaint coastal resorts with attractive harbours and maritime activities. The stunning Snowdonia National Park, right at its centre, covers 823 miles of beautiful, unspoilt countryside and a wide range of leisure activities can be enjoyed. Natural attractions abound throughout the area - mountains, forests, lakes, rivers and waterfalls all wait to be explored, and man-made attractions include castles, railways and industrial archaeology.

Abersoch, Anglesey, Beaumaris, Caernarfon, Criccieth

ABERSOCH. Around the magnificent Welsh Coast. Away from the madding crowd. Near safe sandy beaches. A small specialist agency offering privacy, peace and unashamed luxury. First Wales Tourist Board Self Catering Gold Award Winner. Residential standards - Dishwashers, Microwaves, Washing Machines, Central Heating, Log Fires, No Slot Meters. Linen provided. Pets welcome free. All in coastal areas famed for scenery, walks, wild flowers, birds, badgers and foxes. Free colour brochure.

SB S.C. Rees, "Quality Cottages", Cerbid, Solva, Haverfordwest, Pembrokeshire SA62 6YE (01348 837871). website: www.qualitycottages.co.uk

SB

Ingledene Bach

"Ingledene Bach", our holiday cottage is to the rear of the main house which is run as a B&B. Originally the servants' quarters, the cottage, which sleeps 2 adults and 2 children, is light and airy and close to the beach, providing a perfect base for a traditional seaside holiday. Downstairs: fully fitted kitchen, dining area, sitting room and bathroom. Upstairs: double bedroom and children's room with bunk beds (the sea can be seen from both rooms). Bedding and towels provided. Outside, guests have use of the garden and barbecue area with ample parking and room for boats. *Prices from £175 - £495 per week. Non-smoking. Sorry, no pets.*

Richard and Shirley Murphy, Ingledene Bach, Ravenspoint Road, Trearddur Bay LL65 2YU
Tel: 01407 861026
e-mail: info@ingledene.co.uk • www.ingledene.co.uk

BEAUMARIS. Around the magnificent Welsh Coast. Away from the madding crowd. Near safe sandy beaches. A small specialist agency offering privacy, peace and unashamed luxury. First Wales Tourist Board Self Catering Gold Award Winner. Residential standards - Dishwashers, Microwaves, Washing Machines, Central Heating, Log Fires, No Slot Meters. Linen provided. Pets welcome free. All in coastal areas famed for scenery, walks, wild flowers, birds, badgers and foxes. Free colour brochure.

SB S.C. Rees, "Quality Cottages", Cerbid, Solva, Haverfordwest, Pembrokeshire SA62 6YE (01348 837871). website: www.qualitycottages.co.uk

Plas-Y-Bryn Chalet Park Bontnewydd, Near Caernarfon LL54 7YE (01286 672811)

Our small park is situated two miles from the historic town of Caernarfon. Set into a walled garden it offers safety, seclusion and beautiful views of Snowdonia. It is ideally positioned for touring the area. Shop and village pub nearby. A selection of chalets and caravans available at prices from £120 (low season) to £430 (high season) per week for the caravans and £120 (low season) to £550 (high season) per week for the chalets. Well behaved pets always welcome. **WTB ★★★★**

e-mail: philplasybryn@aol.com • www.plasybrynholidayscaernarfon.co.uk

CRICCIETH. Around the magnificent Welsh Coast. Away from the madding crowd. Near safe sandy beaches. A small specialist agency offering privacy, peace and unashamed luxury. First Wales Tourist Board Self Catering Gold Award Winner. Residential standards - Dishwashers, Microwaves, Washing Machines, Central Heating, Log Fires, No Slot Meters. Linen provided. Pets welcome free. All in coastal areas famed for scenery, walks, wild flowers, birds, badgers and foxes. Free colour brochure.

SB S.C. Rees, "Quality Cottages", Cerbid, Solva, Haverfordwest, Pembrokeshire SA62 6YE (01348 837871). website: www.qualitycottages.co.uk

FREE or REDUCED RATE entry to Holiday Visits and Attractions – see our
READERS' OFFER VOUCHERS on pages 193-230

Criccieth, Harlech, Porthmadog, Trearddur Bay

North Wales

Formby

Crosby
Bootle
Wallasey

Birkenhead
A540

Anglesey

Great
Ormes
Head

Prestatyn

River Dee

Mersey

LIVERPOOL

Llandudno Colwyn
Bay Rhyl
A55 A548

Holywell
A548

Ellesmere
Port
A41

Runcorn

M56 Frodsham

A49

Beaumaris Conwy

Bangor Llanfairfechan
A55 Abergele
A548 St Asaph
A525 A541 Flint
Queensferry Middl
Chester A54

A4244
Bethesda
A5
A470 Denbigh
A544 A541 A55 Winsford
CHESHIRE

anberis Llanrwst CONWY
A543 Mold
A494 FLINTSHIRE
A483 A41
A51

A4086
Betws-
y-coed
A498 A470 A5 Ruthin
DENBIGHSHIRE
A525 A5104 Nantwich

A4085

Blaenau
Ffestiniog
A4085 A5 A494 A5104 A542 Ruabon
Wrexham
WREXHAM A41 A49 A530

A498 Ffestiniog
A4212 A483 A525
Llangollen
Whitchurch

Porthmadog Bala A494 A539 A495
ieth A528 Ellesmere A41
A470 A5 A495
GWYNEDD Oswestry Wem A49 A53
A496 A528

Please note

Conwy, Llandonna, Morfa Nefyn, Penmaenmawr

LLANDONNA. Around the magnificent Welsh Coast. Away from the madding crowd. Near safe sandy beaches. A small specialist agency offering privacy, peace and unashamed luxury. First Wales Tourist Board Self Catering Gold Award Winner. Residential standards - Dishwashers, Microwaves, Washing Machines, Central Heating, Log Fires, No Slot Meters. Linen provided. Pets welcome free. All in coastal areas famed for scenery, walks, wild flowers, birds, badgers and foxes. Free colour brochure.
S.C. Rees, "Quality Cottages", Cerbid, Solva, Haverfordwest, Pembrokeshire SA62 6YE (01348 837871). SB
website: www.qualitycottages.co.uk

MORFA NEFYN. Around the magnificent Welsh Coast. Away from the madding crowd. Near safe sandy beaches. A small specialist agency offering privacy, peace and unashamed luxury. First Wales Tourist Board Self Catering Gold Award Winner. Residential standards - Dishwashers, Microwaves, Washing Machines, Central Heating, Log Fires, No Slot Meters. Linen provided. Pets welcome free. All in coastal areas famed for scenery, walks, wild flowers, birds, badgers and foxes. Free colour brochure.
S.C. Rees, "Quality Cottages", Cerbid, Solva, Haverfordwest, Pembrokeshire SA62 6YE (01348 837871). SB
website: www.qualitycottages.co.uk

Carmarthenshire

Pen Y Banc Cottage
Llanfihangel ar Arth, Llandysul

Lovely isolated, cosy bungalow on owner's organic farm. Ideal for walking and touring Brecon Beacons, Pembrokeshire Coastal Footpath and Black Mountains. Sleeps 4, one double and one twin bedroom. Oil fired, two oven Rayburn cooker in beamed open plan sitting/dining room. All heating/electric costs included in price. Brochure available. Non smoking.

Penny & Graeme Whitaker
Tel: 01559 384515 • Fax: 01559 389034
Gwhit34925@aol.com • www.solutions-factory.co.uk/penybanccottage

Looking for Holiday Accommodation?

for details of hundreds of properties throughout the UK, visit our website

www.holidayguides.com

Ceredigion

Aberporth, Cardigan Bay, Llangrannog

ABERPORTH. Around the magnificent Welsh Coast. Away from the madding crowd. Near safe sandy beaches. A small specialist agency offering privacy, peace and unashamed luxury. First Wales Tourist Board Self Catering Gold Award Winner. Residential standards - Dishwashers, Microwaves, Washing Machines, Central Heating, Log Fires, No Slot Meters. Linen provided. Pets welcome free. All in coastal areas famed for scenery, walks, wild flowers, birds, badgers and foxes. Free colour brochure.
S.C. Rees, "Quality Cottages", Cerbid, Solva, Haverfordwest, Pembrokeshire SA62 6YE (01348 837871). SB
website: www.qualitycottages.co.uk

LLANGRANNOG. Around the magnificent Welsh Coast. Away from the madding crowd. Near safe sandy beaches. A small specialist agency offering privacy, peace and unashamed luxury. First Wales Tourist Board Self Catering Gold Award Winner. Residential standards - Dishwashers, Microwaves, Washing Machines, Central Heating, Log Fires, No Slot Meters. Linen provided. Pets welcome free. All in coastal areas famed for scenery, walks, wild flowers, birds, badgers and foxes. Free colour brochure.
S.C. Rees, "Quality Cottages", Cerbid, Solva, Haverfordwest, Pembrokeshire SA62 6YE (01348 837871). SB
website: www.qualitycottages.co.uk

Pembrokeshire

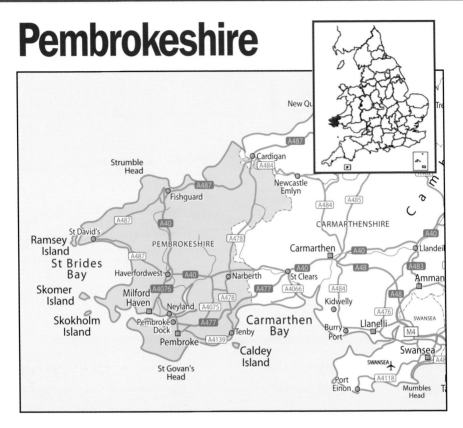

PEMBROKESHIRE'S entire coastline is a designated National Park, with its sheltered coves and wooded estuaries, fine sandy beaches and some of the most dramatic cliffs in Britain. The islands of Skomer, Stokholm and Grasholm are home to thousands of seabirds, and Ramsey Island, as well as being an RSPB Reserve boasts the second largest grey seal colony in Britain. Pembrokeshire's mild climate and the many delightful towns and villages, family attractions and outdoor facilities such as surfing, water skiing, diving, pony trekking and fishing make this a favourite holiday destination.

Bosherton, Haverfordwest

BOSHERTON. Around the magnificent Welsh Coast. Away from the madding crowd. Near safe sandy beaches. A small specialist agency offering privacy, peace and unashamed luxury. First Wales Tourist Board Self Catering Gold Award Winner. Residential standards - Dishwashers, Microwaves, Washing Machines, Central Heating, Log Fires, No Slot Meters. Linen provided. Pets welcome free. All in coastal areas famed for scenery, walks, wild flowers, birds, badgers and foxes. Free colour brochure.
S.C. Rees, "Quality Cottages", Cerbid, Solva, Haverfordwest, Pembrokeshire SA62 6YE (01348 837871).
website: www.qualitycottages.co.uk

SB

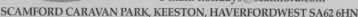

Llanteg, Newgale, Newport, St Davids, Solva

LLANTEGLOS ESTATE

WTB ★★★★

Charming self-contained Woodland Lodges (sleep up to 6) set in quiet countryside estate. Views over National Parkland and Carmarthen Bay from balconies. Ideal for holidays or shorter breaks in any season. Safe children's play area. Elsewhere on the property, visit our wonderful rustic clubhouse - 'The Wanderer's Rest Inn', with fully licensed bar, roaring fire, food and entertainment. Miles of sandy beaches, many visitor attractions for all ages and rambling trails close by. A warm welcome awaits you. For further details and colour brochure please telephone Tony and Jane Baron.

TONY & JANE BARON, LLANTEGLOS ESTATE, LLANTEG, NEAR AMROTH, PEMBROKESHIRE SA67 8PU • Tel: 01834 831677/831371
e-mail: llanteglosestate@supanet.com • www.llanteglos-estate.com

NEWGALE. Around the magnificent Welsh Coast. Away from the madding crowd. Near safe sandy beaches. A small specialist agency offering privacy, peace and unashamed luxury. First Wales Tourist Board Self Catering Gold Award Winner. Residential standards - Dishwashers, Microwaves, Washing Machines, Central Heating, Log Fires, No Slot Meters. Linen provided. Pets welcome free. All in coastal areas famed for scenery, walks, wild flowers, birds, badgers and foxes. Free colour brochure.
SB **S.C. Rees, "Quality Cottages", Cerbid, Solva, Haverfordwest, Pembrokeshire SA62 6YE (01348 837871).**
website: www.qualitycottages.co.uk

NEWPORT. Around the magnificent Welsh Coast. Away from the madding crowd. Near safe sandy beaches. A small specialist agency offering privacy, peace and unashamed luxury. First Wales Tourist Board Self Catering Gold Award Winner. Residential standards - Dishwashers, Microwaves, Washing Machines, Central Heating, Log Fires, No Slot Meters. Linen provided. Pets welcome free. All in coastal areas famed for scenery, walks, wild flowers, birds, badgers and foxes. Free colour brochure.
SB **S.C. Rees, "Quality Cottages", Cerbid, Solva, Haverfordwest, Pembrokeshire SA62 6YE (01348 837871).**
website: www.qualitycottages.co.uk

ST DAVIDS. Around the magnificent Welsh Coast. Away from the madding crowd. Near safe sandy beaches. A small specialist agency offering privacy, peace and unashamed luxury. First Wales Tourist Board Self Catering Gold Award Winner. Residential standards - Dishwashers, Microwaves, Washing Machines, Central Heating, Log Fires, No Slot Meters. Linen provided. Pets welcome free. All in coastal areas famed for scenery, walks, wild flowers, birds, badgers and foxes. Free colour brochure.
SB **S.C. Rees, "Quality Cottages", Cerbid, Solva, Haverfordwest, Pembrokeshire SA62 6YE (01348 837871).**
website: www.qualitycottages.co.uk

SOLVA. Around the magnificent Welsh Coast. Away from the madding crowd. Near safe sandy beaches. A small specialist agency offering privacy, peace and unashamed luxury. First Wales Tourist Board Self Catering Gold Award Winner. Residential standards - Dishwashers, Microwaves, Washing Machines, Central Heating, Log Fires, No Slot Meters. Linen provided. Pets welcome free. All in coastal areas famed for scenery, walks, wild flowers, birds, badgers and foxes. Free colour brochure.
SB **S.C. Rees, "Quality Cottages", Cerbid, Solva, Haverfordwest, Pembrokeshire SA62 6YE (01348 837871).**
website: www.qualitycottages.co.uk

Publisher's note

While every effort is made to ensure accuracy, we regret that FHG Guides cannot accept responsibility for errors, misrepresentations or omissions in our entries or any consequences thereof. Prices in particular should be checked.
We will follow up complaints but cannot act as arbiters or agents for either party.

TENBY. Around the magnificent Welsh Coast. Away from the madding crowd. Near safe sandy beaches. A small specialist agency offering privacy, peace and unashamed luxury. First Wales Tourist Board Self Catering Gold Award Winner. Residential standards - Dishwashers, Microwaves, Washing Machines, Central Heating, Log Fires, No Slot Meters. Linen provided. Pets welcome free. All in coastal areas famed for scenery, walks, wild flowers, birds, badgers and foxes. Free colour brochure.

S.C. Rees, "Quality Cottages", Cerbid, Solva, Haverfordwest, Pembrokeshire SA62 6YE (01348 837871). website: **www.qualitycottages.co.uk**

SB

A country estate of over 450 acres, including 2 miles of riverbank. See a real farm in action, the hustle and bustle of harvest, newborn calves and lambs. Choose from 6 character stone cottages, lovingly converted traditional farm buildings, some over 200 years old.

www.davidsfarm.com

Each cottage is fully furnished and equipped, electricity and linen included, with all year round heating. Children welcome. Brochure available. Contact: **Mrs Angela Colledge, Gwarmacwydd, Llanfallteg, Whitland, Pembrokeshire SA34 0XH**

Self Catering ★★★★ Cottages t **01437 563 260**

SB

Other specialised holiday guides from FHG

Recommended **INNS & PUBS** OF BRITAIN

Recommended **COUNTRY HOTELS** OF BRITAIN

Recommended **SHORT BREAK HOLIDAYS** IN BRITAIN

The bestselling and original **PETS WELCOME!**

The **GOLF GUIDE,** *Where to Play, Where to Stay* IN BRITAIN & IRELAND

COAST & COUNTRY HOLIDAYS

BED & BREAKFAST STOPS

CARAVAN & CAMPING HOLIDAYS

CHILDREN WELCOME! Family Holiday & Days Out Guide

BRITAIN'S BEST LEISURE & RELAXATION GUIDE

Published annually: available in all good bookshops or direct from the publisher:

FHG Guides, Abbey Mill Business Centre, Seedhill, Paisley PA1 1TJ

Tel: 0141 887 0428 • Fax: 0141 889 7204

E-mail: admin@fhguides.co.uk • Web: www.holidayguides.com

Powys

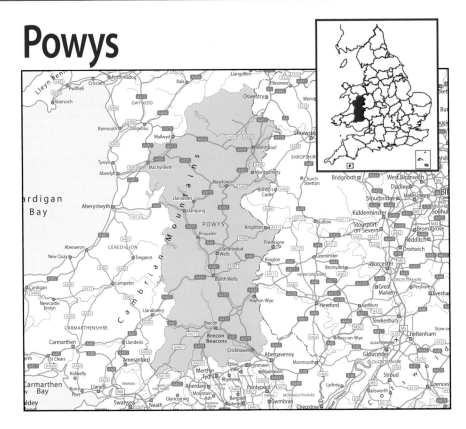

POWYS is situated right on England's doorstep and boasts some of the most spectacular scenery in Europe. Ideal for an action packed holiday with fishing, golfing, pony trekking, sailing and canal cruising readily available, and walkers have a choice of everything from riverside trails to mountain hikes. Offa's Dyke Path and Glyndwr's Way pass through the region. Offa's Dyke Path runs for 177 miles through Border country, often following the ancient earthworks, while Glyndwr's Way takes in some of the finest landscape features in Wales on its journey from Knighton to Machynlleth and back to the borders at Welshpool.

There are border towns with Georgian architecture and half-timbered black and white houses to visit, or wander round the wonderful shops in the book town of Hay, famous for its Literary Festival each May. There are Victorian spa towns too, with even the smallest of places holding festivals and events throughout the year.

The FHG Directory of Website Addresses
on pages 169-191 is a useful quick reference guide for holiday accommodation with e-mail and/or website details

Garthmyl, Hay-on-Wye, Knighton, Llandrindod Wells

Ireland

County Clare

Ballyvaughan Village and Country Holiday Homes

Offering a wide range of quality self-catering holiday accommodation in the unspoilt and charming village of Ballyvaughan on the southern shores of Galway Bay in the heartland of the world famous Burren district of County Clare. You can choose from our four-star cottages, which sleep up to six, or one of our apartments, which sleep up to three. All our village accommodation is located in the centre of the village with a good choice of restaurants and pubs. Our location is an ideal base to explore the unique Burren landscape or tour the west coast of Ireland. All our accommodation is available all year and is very suitable for off-season bookings.

Visit our comprehensive website for more details. Terms from €299 to €799.

**Mr George Quinn, Main Street, Ballyvaughan, Co.Clare • 00353 659 051977
e-mail: vchh@iol.ie • www.ballyvaughan-cottages.com**

SB

symbols

	Totally non-smoking		Pets Welcome
	Children Welcome	**SB**	Short Breaks
	Suitable for Disabled Guests	♉	Licensed

Ratings & Awards

For the first time ever the AA, VisitBritain, VisitScotland, and the Wales Tourist Board will use a single method of assessing and rating serviced accommodation. Irrespective of which organisation inspects an establishment the rating awarded will be the same, using a common set of standards, giving a clear guide of what to expect. The RAC is no longer operating an Hotel inspection and accreditation business.

Accommodation Standards: Star Grading Scheme

Using a scale of 1-5 stars the objective quality ratings give a clear indication of accommodation standard, cleanliness, ambience, hospitality, service and food, This shows the full range of standards suitable for every budget and preference, and allows visitors to distinguish between the quality of accommodation and facilities on offer in different establishments. All types of board and self-catering accommodation are covered, including hotels,
B&Bs, holiday parks, campus accommodation, hostels, caravans and camping, and boats.

VisitBritain and the regional tourist boards, enjoyEngland.com, VisitScotland and VisitWales, and the AA have full details of the grading system on their websites

The more stars, the higher level of quality

★★★★★
exceptional quality, with a degree of luxury

★★★★
excellent standard throughout

★★★
very good level of quality and comfort

★★
good quality, well presented and well run

★
acceptable quality; simple, practical, no frills

National Accessible Scheme

If you have particular mobility, visual or hearing needs, look out for the National Accessible Scheme. You can be confident of finding accommodation or attractions that meet your needs by looking for the following symbols.

 Typically suitable for a person with sufficient mobility to climb a flight of steps but would benefit from fixtures and fittings to aid balance

 Typically suitable for a person with restricted walking ability and for those that may need to use a wheelchair some of the time and can negotiate a maximum of three steps

 Typically suitable for a person who depends on the use of a wheelchair and transfers unaided to and from the wheelchair in a seated position. This person may be an independent traveller

 Typically suitable for a person who depends on the use of a wheelchair in a seated position. This person also requires personal or mechanical assistance (eg carer, hoist).

Caravans & Camping

Cornwall

CORNWALL. St Ives Bay Holiday Park, Upton Towans, Hayle TR27 5BH (0800 317713).
The park on the beach. St Ives Bay Holiday Park is set in sand dunes which run down to its own sandy beach. Many units have superb sea views. There is a large indoor pool and 2 clubs with FREE entertainment on the Park.
www.stivesbay.co.uk

Crackington Haven, St Agnes

Cumbria (opposite)

Devon

Isle of Wight

Ryde

Brean, Minehead

Somerset

SCOTLAND
Caravan & Camping
Angus & Dundee

Brechin

BRECHIN. Scott Murray, Eastmill Caravan Park, Brechin DD9 7EL (01356 625206; out of season 01356 622487; Fax: 01356 623356).
Beautifully situated on flat grassy site along the River South Esk, within easy access of scenic Angus Glens, local walks and 10 miles from sandy east coast beaches; midway between Dundee and Aberdeen. Shop, gas supplies, shower block, laundry and hook-ups on site; licensed premises nearby. Six-berth caravans with mains services available to rent. Facilities for tourers, caravanettes and tents.
• Open April to October. • Dogs welcome.

Highlands

Lairg

Dunroamin
Caravan Park
Main Street, Lairg IV27 4AR

Lew Hudson, his wife Margaret and their family welcome you to Dunroamin Caravan Park. A small family-run park situated in the picturesque village of Lairg by Loch Shin, this is the ideal base for touring the whole of Sutherland and Caithness. Fishing and walking nearby, with golf just 15 miles away.
Outstandingly well maintained grounds with Crofters licensed restaurant on site. Electric hook-ups. 200 yards from pub, bank, shops, post office, etc. Holiday caravans for hire, tourers and tents welcome.

Tel: 01549 402447
enquiries@lairgcaravanpark.co.uk
www.lairgcaravanpark.co.uk

Looking for holiday accommodation?
for details of hundreds of properties
throughout the UK visit:
www.holidayguides.com

WALES
Caravan & Camping
Anglesey & Gwynedd

Isle of Anglesey

IRELAND
Caravan & Camping
County Kerry

Lauragh

Mrs M. Moriarty, Creveen Lodge, Healy Pass Road, Lauragh (00 353 64 83131; from Ireland 064 83131). Immaculately run small hill farm overlooking Kenmare Bay in a striking area of County Kerry. Reception is found at the Lodge, which also offers guests a comfortable sitting room, while a separate block has well equipped and immaculately maintained toilets and showers, plus a communal room with a large fridge, freezer and ironing facilities. The park is carefully tended, with bins and picnic tables informally placed, plus a children's play area with slides and swings. There are twenty pitches in total, 16 for tents and four for caravans, with an area of hardstanding for motorcaravans. Electrical connections are available. Fishing, bicycle hire, water sports and horse riding available nearby. SAE please, for replies.
e-mail: info@creveenlodge.com
website: www.creveenlodge.com

symbols

	Totally non-smoking	🐕	Pets Welcome
	Children Welcome	**SB**	Short Breaks
	Suitable for Disabled Guests	♀	Licensed

Visit the FHG website
www.holidayguides.com
for details of the wide choice of accommodation
featured in the full range of FHG titles

DIRECTORY OF WEBSITE AND E-MAIL ADDRESSES

A quick-reference guide to holiday accommodation with an e-mail address and/or website, conveniently arranged by country and county, with full contact details.

Self-Catering Apartments
Mary & Simon Ette, The Independent Traveller, 8 The Glebe, Thorverton, Exeter EX5 5LS
Tel: 01392 860807
• e-mail: help@gowithit.co.uk
• website: www.gowithit.co.uk

•LONDON

Hotel
Athena Hotel, 110-114 Sussex Gardens, Hyde Park, LONDON W2 1UA
Tel: 020 7706 3866
• e-mail: athena@stavrouhotels.co.uk
• website: www.stavrouhotels.co.uk

Hotel
Elizabeth Hotel, 37 Eccleston Square, LONDON SW1V 1PB Tel: 020 7828 6812
• e-mail: info@elizabethhotel.com
• website: www.elizabethhotel.com

Hotel
Gower Hotel, 129 Sussex Gardens, Hyde Park, LONDON W2 2RX
Tel: 020 7262 2262
• e-mail: gower@stavrouhotels.co.uk
• website: www.stavrouhotels.co.uk

B & B
Manor Court Hotel, 7 Clanricarde Gardens, LONDON W2 4JJ Tel: 020 7792 3361 or 020 7727 5407
• e-mail: enquiries@manorcourthotel.com
• website: www.abc-london.com
            www.123europe-londonhotels.com

Hotel
Queens Hotel, 33 Anson Road, Tufnell Park, LONDON N7 Tel: 020 7607 4725
• e-mail: queens@stavrouhotels.co.uk
• website: www.stavrouhotels.co.uk

•BERKSHIRE

Guest House
Clarence Hotel, 9 Clarence Road, WINDSOR, Berkshire SL4 5AE
Tel: 01753 864436
• e-mail: clarence.hotel@btconnect.com
• website: www.clarence-hotel.co.uk

•BUCKINGHAMSHIRE

B & B / Self-Catering Cottages
Poletrees Farm, Ludgershall Road, Brill, AYLESBURY, Buckinghamshire HP18 9TZ
Tel: 01844 238276
• e-mail: poletrees.farm@virgin.net
• web: www.country-accom.co.uk/poletrees-farm

•CAMBRIDGESHIRE

Self-Catering
Hilary's Cottage, CAMBRIDGE.
Contact: Mrs H. Marsh, The Meadow House, 2A High Street, BURWELL, Cambridgeshire CB25 0HB
Tel: 01638 741926
• e-mail: hilary@themeadowhouse.co.uk
• website: www.themeadowhouse.co.uk

B & B
Mrs Hatley, Manor Farm, Landbeach, CAMBRIDGE, Cambridgeshire CB4 8ED
Tel: 01223 860165
• e-mail: vhatley@btinternet.com
• website: www.smoothhound.co.uk/hotels/manorfarm4

www.holidayguides.com

•CHESHIRE

Guest House / Self-Catering

Mrs Joanne Hollins, Balterley Green Farm,
Deans Lane, BALTERLEY, near Crewe
Cheshire CW2 5QJ Tel: 01270 820 214
• e-mail: greenfarm@balterley.fsnet.co.uk
• website: www.greenfarm.freeserve.co.uk

B & B

Needhams Farm, Uplands Road, Werneth
Low, Gee Cross, HYDE (near Manchester),
Cheshire SK14 3AG Tel: 0161 3684610
• e-mail: charlotte@needhamsfarm.co.uk

•CORNWALL

Self-Catering

Cornish Traditional Cottages, Blisland,
BODMIN, Cornwall PL30 4HS
Tel: 01208 821666
• e-mail: info@corncott.com
• website: www.corncott.com

Self-Catering

Penrose Burden Holiday Cottages,
St Breward, BODMIN, Cornwall PL30 4LZ
Tel: 01208 850277 or 01208 850617
• website: www.penroseburden.co.uk

Self-Catering

Henwood Barns, Henwood, BODMIN
MOOR, Cornwall PL14 5BP
Tel: 01579 363 576
• e-mail: henwoodbarns@tiscali.co.uk
• website: www.henwoodbarns.co.uk

Hotel

Stratton Gardens Hotel, Cot Hill, Stratton,
BUDE, Cornwall EX23 9DN Tel: 01288
352500
• e-mail: moira@stratton-gardens.co.uk
• website: www.stratton-gardens.co.uk

Self-Catering

Mineshop Holiday Cottages,
CRACKINGTON HAVEN, Bude,
Cornwall EX23 0NR Tel: 01840 230338
• e-mail: tippett@mineshop.freeserve.co.uk
• website: www.mineshop.co.uk

Self-Catering

Mr M. Watson, Creekside Cottages,
Restronguet, Near FALMOUTH, Cornwall
Tel: 01326 375972
• e-mail: martin@creeksidecottages.co.uk
• website: www.creeksidecottages.co.uk

Self-Catering

Mr P. Watson, Creekside Holiday Houses,
Restronguet, FALMOUTH, Cornwall
Tel: 01326 372722
• website: www.creeksideholidayhouses.co.uk

Hotel

Rosemullion Hotel, Gyllyngvase Hill,
FALMOUTH, Cornwall TR11 4DF
Tel: 01326 314 690
• e-mail: gail@rosemullionhotel.demon.co.uk
• www.SmoothHound.co.uk/hotels/rosemullion.

Self-Catering

Mrs K Terry, "Shasta", Carwinion Road,
Mawnan Smith, FALMOUTH, Cornwall
TR11 5JD Tel: 01326 250775
• e-mail: katerry@btopenworld.com

Guest House

Jenny Lake, Wickham Guest House,
21 Gyllyngvase Terrace, FALMOUTH,
Cornwall TR11 4DL Tel: 01326 311140
• e-mail:
enquiries@wickhamhotel.freeserve.co.uk
• website: www.wickham-hotel.co.uk

Caravan Park

St Ives Bay Holiday Park, Upton Towans,
HAYLE, Cornwall TR27 5BH
Tel: 0800 317713
• website: www.stivesbay.co.uk

Self-Catering / Campsite

Franchis Holidays, Cury Cross Lanes,
Mullion, HELSTON, Cornwall TR12 7AZ
Tel: 01326 240301
• e-mail: enquiries@franchis.co.uk
• website: www.franchis.co.uk

Static Caravan & Camping

Little Trevothan Caravan Park, Coverack,
NEAR HELSTON, Cornwall TR12 6SD
Tel: 01326 280260
• e-mail: sales@littletrevothan.co.uk
• website: www.littletrevothan.co.uk

Readers are requested to mention this FHG
guidebook when seeking accommodation

Self-Catering
Celia Hutchinson,
Caradon Country Cottages, East Taphouse,
LISKEARD, Cornwall PL14 4NH
Tel: 01579 320355
• e-mail: celia@caradoncottages.co.uk
• website: www.caradoncottages.co.uk

Self-Catering
Tracy Dennett, Talehay Holiday Cottages,
Pelynt, Near LOOE, Cornwall PL13 2LT
Tel: 01503 220252
• e-mail: infobookings@talehay.co.uk
• website: www.talehay.co.uk

Holiday Park
Tregoad Park, St Martins, LOOE, Cornwall
PL13 1PB Tel: 01503 262718
• e-mail: info@tregoadpark.co.uk
• website: www.tregoadpark.co.uk

Self-Catering
Mr & Mrs Holder, Valleybrook Holidays,
Peakswater, Lansallos, LOOE,
Cornwall PL13 2QE Tel: 01503 220493
• website: www.valleybrookholidays.com

Self-Catering Cottages
Wringworthy Cottages, LOOE, Cornwall
PL13 1PR Tel: 01503 240 685
• e-mail: pets@wringworthy.co.uk
• website: www.wringworthy.co.uk

Self-catering Lodges
Blue Bay Lodge, Trenance, MAWGAN
PORTH, Cornwall TR8 4DA
Tel: 01637 860324
• e-mail: hotel@bluebaycornwall.co.uk
• website: www.bluebaycornwall.co.uk

B & B
Mrs Dawn Rundle, Lancallan Farm,
MEVAGISSEY, St Austell,Cornwall PL26
6EW Tel: 01726 842 284
• e-mail: dawn@lancallan.fsnet.co.uk
• website: www.lancallanfarm.co.uk

Guest House
Mrs Dewolfreys, Dewolf Guest House, 100
Henver Road, NEWQUAY, Cornwall TR7 3BL
Tel: 01637 874746
• e-mail: holidays@dewolfguesthouse.com
• website: www.dewolfguesthouse.com

Guest House
Pensalda Guest House, 98 Henver Road,
NEWQUAY, Cornwall TR7 3BL
Tel: 01637 874 601
• e-mail: karen_pensalda@yahoo.co.uk
• website: www.pensalda-guesthouse.co.uk

Caravan & Camping / Self-Catering
Quarryfield Caravan & Camping Park,
Crantock, NEWQUAY, Cornwall
Contact: Mrs A. Winn, Tretherras, Newquay,
Cornwall TR7 2RE
Tel: 01637 872 792
• website: www.quarryfield.co.uk

Hotel
St George's Hotel, 71 Mount Wise,
NEWQUAY, Cornwall TR7 2BP
Tel: 01637 873010
• e-mail:
enquiries@stgeorgeshotel.free-online.co.uk
• website: www.st-georges-newquay.co.uk

Self-Catering
Raintree House Holidays, Whistlers,
Treyarnon Bay, PADSTOW, Cornwall PL28
8JR Tel: 01841 520228
• e-mail: gill@raintreehouse.co.uk
• website: www.raintreehouse.co.uk

Hotel
Tregea Hotel, 16-18 High Street, PADSTOW,
Cornwall PL28 8BB Tel: 01841 532 455
• e-mail: enquiries@tregea.co.uk
• website: www.tregea.co.uk

Guest House
Lynda Sowerby, Torwood House, Alexandra
Road, PENZANCE, Cornwall TR18 4LZ
Tel: 01736 360063
• e-mail: lyndasowerby@aol.com
• website: www.torwoodhousehotel.co.uk

Hotel
Rosevine Hotel, Porthcurnick Beach,
PORTSCATHO, Near St Mawes,
Cornwall TR2 5EW Tel: 01872 580206
• e-mail: info@rosevine.co.uk
• website: www.rosevine.co.uk

Caravan & Camping / Holiday Park
Chiverton Park, Blackwater, ST AGNES,
Cornwall TR4 8HS Tel: 01872 560667
• e-mail: info@chivertonpark.co.uk
• website: www.chivertonpark.co.uk

Hotel / Inn
Driftwood Spars Hotel, Trevaunance Cove,
ST AGNES, Cornwall TR5 0RT
Tel: 01872 552428
• website: www.driftwoodspars.com

Hotel / B & B
Penkerris, Penwinnick Road, ST AGNES,
Cornwall TR5 0PA Tel: 01872 552262
• e-mail: info@penkerris.co.uk
• website: www.penkerris.co.uk

Guest House
Mr Gardener, The Elms, 14 Penwinnick
Road, ST AUSTELL, Cornwall PL25 5DW
Tel: 01726 74981
• e-mail: pete@edenbb.co.uk
• website: www.edenbb.co.uk

Self-Catering
Mr & Mrs C.W. Pestell, Hockadays,
Tregenna, Near Blisland, ST TUDY,
Cornwall PL30 4QJ Tel: 01208 850146
• website: www.hockadays.co.uk

Self-Catering
Mrs R. Reeves, Polstraul, Trewalder,
Delabole, ST TUDY, Cornwall PL33 9ET
Tel: 01840 213 120
• e-mail: ruth.reeves@hotmail.co.uk
• website: www.maymear.co.uk

Self-Catering
Mrs Sandy Wilson, Salutations, Atlantic
Road, TINTAGEL, Cornwall PL34 0DE
Tel: 01840 770287
• e-mail: sandyanddave@tinyworld.co.uk
• website: www.salutationstintagel.co.uk

Farm B & B
Mrs E. Hodge, Pengelly Farmhouse,
Pengelly Farm, Burlawn, WADEBRIDGE,
Cornwall PL27 7LA
Tel: 01208 814 217
• e-mail: hodgepete@hotmail.com
• website: www.pengellyfarm.co.uk

Self- catering
Great Bodieve Farm Barns, WADEBRIDGE,
Cornwall.
Contact: Mrs T Riddle, Molesworth House,
Wadebridge, Cornwall PL27 7SE
Tel: 01208 814916
• e-mail: enquiries@great-bodieve.co.uk
• website: www.great-bodieve.co.uk

•CUMBRIA

Caravan Park
Greenhowe Caravan Park, Great Langdale,
AMBLESIDE, Cumbria LA22 9JU
Tel: 015394 37231
• e-mail: enquiries@greenhowe.com
• website: www.greenhowe.com

Hotel / Guest House
Ian & Helen Burt, The Old Vicarage,
Vicarage Road, AMBLESIDE, Cumbria
LA22 9DH. Tel: 015394 33364
• e-mail: info@oldvicarageambleside.co.uk
• website: www.oldvicarageambleside.co.uk

Hotel
Rothay Manor Hotel, Rothay Bridge,
AMBLESIDE, Cumbria LL22 OEH
Tel: 01539 433605
• e-mail: hotel@rothaymanor.co.uk
• website: www.rothaymanor.co.uk

Self-Catering
43A Quarry Rigg, BOWNESS-ON-
WINDERMERE, Cumbria.
Contact: Mrs E. Jones, 45 West Oakhill Park,
Liverpool L13 4BN Tel: 0151 228 5799
• e-mail: eejay@btinternet.com

B & B
Amanda Vickers, Mosser Heights, Mosser,
COCKERMOUTH, Cumbria CA13 0SS
Tel: 01900 822644
• e-mail: amandavickers1@aol.com
• website: www.stayonacumbrianfarm.co.uk

Guest House
Rose Cottage Guest House, Lorton Road,
COCKERMOUTH, Cumbria CA13 9DX
Tel: 01900 822189
• website: www.rosecottageguest.co.uk

Self-Catering
Hodyoad Cottage, Cumbria.
Contact: Mrs J. A. Cook, Hodyoad House,
Lamplugh, Near COCKERMOUTH, Cumbria
CA14 4TT Tel: 01946 861338
• e-mail: hodyoad@tiscali.co.uk
• website: www.hodyoad.com

Self-Catering
Mr P. Johnston, The Coppermines & Lakes
Cottages, The Estate Office, The Bridge,
CONISTON, Cumbria LA21 8HJ
Tel: 01539 441765
• e-mail: info@coppermines.co.uk
• website: www.coppermines.co.uk

Self-Catering
Fisherground Farm Holidays, ESKDALE,
Cumbria.
Contact: Ian & Jennifer Hall, Orchard House,
Applethwaite, Keswick, Cumbria CA12 4PN
Tel: 017687 73175
• e-mail: holidays@fisherground.co.uk
• website: www.fisherground.co.uk

Hotel
Hampsfell House Hotel, Hampsfell Road,
GRANGE-OVER-SANDS, Cumbria LA11 6BG
Tel: 015395 32567
• e-mail: enquiries@hampsfellhouse.co.uk
• website: www.hampsfellhouse.co.uk

Self-Catering
Routen House & Little Parrock,
Ennerdale, GRASMERE, Cumbria
Contact: Mrs J. Green Tel: 01604 626383
• e-mail: joanne@routenhouse.co.uk
• website: www.routenhouse.co.uk

Farm / Self-Catering
Mr P. Brown, High Dale Park Farm, High Dale
Park, Satterthwaite, Ulverston, GRIZEDALE
FOREST, Cumbria LA12 8LJ
Tel: 01229 860226
• e-mail: peter@lakesweddingmusic.com
• www.lakesweddingmusic.com/accomm

Self-Catering Cottages
Hideaways, The Square, HAWKSHEAD,
Cumbria LA22 0NZ Tel: 015394 42435
• e-mail: bookings@lakeland-hideaways.co.uk
• website: www.lakeland-hideaways.co.uk

Self-Catering
Derwent Water Marina, Portinscale,
KESWICK, Cumbria CA12 5RF
Tel: 017687 72912
• e-mail: info@derwentwatermarina.co.uk
• website: www.derwentwatermarina.co.uk

Guest House
Mr Taylorson, Rickerby Grange, Portinscale,
KESWICK, Cumbria CA12 5RH
Tel: 017687 72344
• e-mail: stay@rickerbygrange.co.uk
• website: www.rickerbygrange.co.uk

Self-Catering / Farm
Mrs J. M. Almond, Irton House Farm,
Isel, Near KESWICK, Cumbria CA13 9ST
Tel: 017687 76380
• e-mail: joan@irtonhousefarm.co.uk
• website: www.irtonhousefarm.com

Self-Catering
Mrs S.J. Bottom, Crossfield Cottages,
KIRKOSWALD, Penrith, Cumbria CA10 1EU
Tel: 01768 898711
• e-mail: info@crossfieldcottages.co.uk
• website: www.crossfieldcottages.co.uk

Inn
The Britannia Inn, Elterwater, LANGDALE,
Cumbria LA22 9HP Tel: 015394 37210
• e-mail: info@britinn.co.uk
• website: www.britinn.co.uk

Self-Catering
Mr & Mrs Iredale, Carrock Cottages,
Carrock House, Hutton Roof, PENRITH,
Cumbria CA11 0XY Tel: 01768 484111
• e-mail: info@carrockcottages.co.uk
• website: www.carrockcottages.co.uk

Guest House / Inn
Troutbeck Inn, Troutbeck, PENRITH,
Cumbria CA11 0SJ
Tel: 01768 483635
• website: www.thetroutbeckinn.co.uk

Golf Club
Seascale Golf Club, The Banks, SEASCALE,
Cumbria CA20 1QL Tel: 01946 728202
• e-mail: seascalegolfclub@googlemail.com
• website: www.seascalegolfclub.co.uk

Self-Catering / Caravan & Camping
Tanglewood Caravan Park, Causeway Head,
SILLOTH-ON-SOLWAY, Cumbria CA7 4PE
Tel: 016973 31253
• e-mail: tanglewoodcaravanpark@hotmail.com
• website: www.tanglewoodcaravanpark.co.uk

B & B / Self-Catering
Barbara Murphy, Land Ends Country Lodge,
Watermillock, ULLSWATER, Near Penrith,
Cumbria CA11 0NB Tel: 01768 486438
• e-mail: infolandends@btinternet.com
• website: www.landends.co.uk

•DERBYSHIRE

Self-Catering
Patti Cust, The Old Laundry, Sturston Hall,
ASHBOURNE, Derbyshire DE6 1LN
Tel: 01335 346711
• e-mail: p.cust@virgin.net
• website: www.sturston.com

Self-Catering Holiday Cottages
Mark Redfern, Paddock House Farm Holiday
Cottages, Alstonefield, ASHBOURNE,
Derbyshire DE6 2FT Tel: 01335 310282
• e-mail: info@paddockhousefarm.co.uk
• website: www.paddockhousefarm.co.uk

B&B
Mrs J. Salisbury, Turlow Bank, Hognaston,
ASHBOURNE, Derbyshire DE6 1PW
Tel: 01335 370299
•e-mail: turlowbank@w3z.co.uk
•website: www.turlowbank.co.uk

Self-Catering
P. Skemp, Cotterill Farm,
BIGGIN-BY-HARTINGTON, Buxton,
Derbyshire SK17 0DJ Tel: 01298 84447
• e-mail: enquiries@cotterillfarm.co.uk
• website: www.cotterillfarm.co.uk

Hotel
Biggin Hall, Biggin-by-Hartington,
BUXTON, Derbyshire SK17 0DH
Tel: 01298 84451
• e-mail: enquiries@bigginhall.co.uk
• website: www.bigginhall.co.uk

Self-Catering
Mrs Gillian Taylor, Priory Lea Holiday Flats,
50 White Knowle Road, BUXTON,
Derbyshire SK17 9NH Tel: 01298 23737
• e-mail: priorylea@tiscali.co.uk
• website:
www.cressbrook.co.uk/buxton/priorylea

Caravan & Camping Park
Newhaven Caravan & Camping Park,
Newhaven, NEAR BUXTON,
Derbyshire SK17 0DT Tel: 01298 84300
• e-mail: bobmacara@ntlworld.com
• website: www.newhavencaravanpark.co.uk

Guest House
Ivy House Farm Guest House,
STANTON-BY-BRIDGE, Derby,
Derbyshire DE73 7HT Tel: 01332 863152
• e-mail: mary@guesthouse.fsbusiness.co.uk
• website: www.ivy-house-farm.com

•DEVON

Self-Catering
Toad Hall Cottages, DEVON
Tel: 01548 853089 (24 Hours)
• e-mail: thc@toadhallcottages.com
• website: www.toadhallcottages.co.uk

Self-Catering
Farm & Cottage Holidays, DEVON
Tel: 01237 479698
• website: www.holidaycottages.co.uk

B & B
Lynda Richards, Gages Mill, Buckfastleigh
Road, ASHBURTON, Devon TQ13 7JW
Tel: 01364 652391
• e-mail: gagesmill@aol.com
• website: www.gagesmill.co.uk

Self-Catering / Caravan Park
Parkers Farm Holiday Park, Higher Mead
Farm, ASHBURTON, Devon TQ13 7LJ
Tel: 01364 654869
• e-mail: parkersfarm@btconnect.com
• website: www.parkersfarm.co.uk

Self-Catering
Braddon Cottages, ASHWATER, Beaworthy,
Holsworthy, Devon EX21 5EP
Tel: 01409 211350
• e-mail: holidays@braddoncottages.co.uk
• website: www.braddoncottages.co.uk

Self-Catering
North Devon Holiday Homes,
19 Cross Street, BARNSTAPLE,
Devon EX31 1BD Tel: 01271 376322
• e-mail: info@northdevonholidays.co.uk
• website: www.northdevonholidays.co.uk

Hotel
Sandy Cove Hotel, Combe Martin Bay,
BERRYNARBOR, Devon EX34 9SR
Tel: 01271 882243/882888
• website: www.sandycove-hotel.co.uk

Hotel
Yeoldon House Hotel, Durrant Lane,
Northam, BIDEFORD, Devon EX39 2RL
Tel: 01237 474400
• e-mail: yeoldonhouse@aol.com
• website: www.yeoldonhousehotel.co.uk

B & B / Self-Catering
Mr & Mrs Lewin, Lake House Cottages
and B&B, Lake Villa, BRADWORTHY,
Devon EX22 7SQ Tel: 01409 241962
• e-mail: info@lakevilla.co.uk
• website: www.lakevilla.co.uk

Self-Catering / Organic Farm
Little Comfort Farm Cottages,
Little Comfort Farm, BRAUNTON,
North Devon EX33 2NJ Tel: 01271 812414
• e-mail: info@littlecomfortfarm.co.uk
• website: www.littlecomfortfarm.co.uk

Guest House
Woodlands Guest House, Parkham Road,
BRIXHAM, South Devon TQ5 9BU
Tel: 01803 852040
• e-mail: woodlandsbrixham@btinternet.com
• website: www.woodlandsdevon.co.uk

Self-Catering
Amanda Williams, West Banbury Farm
Cottages, BROADWOODWIDGER, NEAR
LIFTON, Devon PL16 0JJ
Tel: 01566 784946
• e-mail: amanda@westbanbury.co.uk
• website: www.westbanbury.co.uk

Self-Catering / B & B / Caravans
Mrs Gould, Bonehayne Farm, COLYTON,
Devon EX24 6SG
Tel: 01404 871416/871396
• e-mail: gould@bonehayne.co.uk
• website: www.bonehayne.co.uk

Self-Catering
Mrs Lee, Church Approach Holidays,
Farway, COLYTON, Devon EX24 6EQ
Tel: 01404 871383/871202
• e-mail: lizlee@eclipse.co.uk
• website: www.churchapproach.co.uk

Self-Catering
Karen Jackson, Boathouse Cottage, Torcross,
DARTMOUTH, Devon TQ7 2TQ
Tel: 01548 580206
• e-mail: enquiries@torcross.com
• website: www.torcross.com

Self-Catering
Mrs S.R. Ridalls, The Old Bakehouse,
7 Broadstone, DARTMOUTH, Devon TQ6 9NR
Tel: 01803 834585
• e-mail: ridallsleisure@aol.com
• website: www.oldbakehousedartmouth.co.uk

Self-Catering
Watermill Cottages, Higher North Mill,
Hansel, DARTMOUTH, Devon TQ6 0LN
Tel: 01803 770219
• e-mail: graham@hanselpg.freeserve.co.uk
• website: www.watermillcottages.co.uk

Self-Catering
Ian West, Station House,
Doddiscombsleigh, EXETER, Devon
EX6 7PW Tel: 01647 253104
• e-mail: enquiries@station-lodge.co.uk
• website: www.station-lodge.co.uk

Self-Catering
Beach Haven, INSTOW, Devon
Contact: Mrs P. I. Barnes, 140 Bay View
Road, Northam, Bideford, Devon EX39 1BJ
Tel: 01237 473801
• website: www.seabirdcottages.co.uk

Self-Catering
Doone Valley Holidays
Contact: Mr C. Harman, Cloud Farm, Oare,
LYNTON, Devon EX35 6NU
Tel: 01598 714234
• e-mail: doonevalleyholidays@hotmail.com
• website: www.doonevalleyholidays.co.uk

Guest House
Mrs T. Williams, Cookshayes, 33 Court
Street, MORETONHAMPSTEAD, Devon
TQ13 8LG Tel: 01647 440374
• e-mail: cookshayes@aol.com
• website: www.cookshayes.co.uk

Farm B & B
Mrs T.M. Merchant, Great Sloncombe Farm,
MORETONHAMPSTEAD, Newton Abbot,
Devon TQ13 8QF Tel: 01647 440595
• e-mail: hmerchant@sloncombe.freeserve.co.uk
• website: www.greatsloncombefarm.co.uk

Self-Catering
Crab Cottage, NOSS MAYO, South Devon
Tel: 01425 471 372
• website: www.crab-cottage.co.uk

Hotel
Christine Clark, Amber House Hotel, 6
Roundham Road, PAIGNTON, Devon TQ4
6EZ Tel: 01803 558372
• e-mail: enquiries@amberhousehotel.co.uk
• website: www.amberhousehotel.co.uk

Guest House
Jane Hill, Beaumont, Castle Hill, SEATON,
Devon EX12 2QW Tel: 01297 20832
• e-mail: jane@lymebay.demon.co.uk
• website:
www.smoothhound.co.uk/beaumon1.html

Camping & Caravan Park
Salcombe Regis Camping & Caravan Park,
Salcombe Regis, SIDMOUTH, Devon
EX10 0JH Tel: 01395 514303
• e-mail: contact@salcombe-regis.co.uk
• website: www.salcombe-regis.co.uk

Self-Catering Lodges
Dartmoor Country Holidays, Magpie Leisure
Park, Horrabridge, Yelverton, TAVISTOCK,
Devon PL20 7RY Tel: 01822 852651
• website: www.dartmoorcountryholidays.co.uk

Caravan & Camping
Harford Bridge Holiday Park, Peter Tavy,
TAVISTOCK, Devon PL19 9LS
Tel: 01822 810349
• e-mail: enquiry@harfordbridge.co.uk
• website: www.harfordbridge.co.uk

Guest House
Mrs Arnold, The Mill, Lower Washfield,
TIVERTON, Devon EX16 9PD
Tel: 01884 255297
• e-mail: themillwashfield@hotmail.co.uk
• website: www.washfield.freeserve.co.uk

Guest House
Mr Butler, Lanscombe House Hotel,
Cockington, TORQUAY, Devon
TQ2 6XA Tel: 01803 606938
• e-mail: stay@lanscombehouse.co.uk
• website: www.lanscombehouse.co.uk

Self-Catering
West Pusehill Farm Cottages,
West Pusehill Farm, Pusehill,
WESTWARD HO!, Devon EX39 5AH
Tel: 01237 475638 or 01237 474622
• e-mail: info@wpfcottages.co.uk
• website: www.wpfcottages.co.uk

Self-Catering
Marsdens Cottage Holidays, 2 The Square,
Braunton, WOOLACOMBE, Devon
EX33 2JB Tel: 01271 813777
• e-mail: holidays@marsdens.co.uk
• website: www.marsdens.co.uk

Holiday Park
Woolacombe Bay Holiday Parcs,
WOOLACOMBE, North Devon
Tel: 01271 870343
• website: www.woolacombe.com/fcw

Caravan & Camping
North Morte Farm Caravan & Camping Park,
Mortehoe, WOOLACOMBE, Devon
EX34 7EG. Tel: 01271 870381
• e-mail: info@northmortefarm.co.uk
• website: www.northmortefarm.co.uk

Farmhouse / B & B
Mrs Linda Landick, Eggworthy Farm,
Sampford Spiney, YELVERTON, Devon
PL20 6LJ Tel: 01822 852142
• e-mail: eggworthyfarm@aol.com
• website: www.eggworthyfarm.co.uk

•DORSET

Self-catering
Dorset Coastal Cottages, The Manor House,
Winfrith Newburgh, Dorchester,
Dorset DT2 8JR Tel: 0800 980 4070
• e-mail: hols@dorsetcoastalcottages.com
• website: www.dorsetcoastalcottages.com

Inn
The Anvil Inn, Salisbury Road, Pimperne,
BLANDFORD, Dorset DT11 8UQ
Tel: 01258 453431
• e-mail: theanvil.inn@btconnect.com
• website: www.anvilinn.co.uk

Hotel
Southbourne Grove Hotel, 96 Southbourne
Road, BOURNEMOUTH, Dorset BH6 3QQ
Tel: 01202 420 503
• e-mail: neil@pack1462.freeserve.co.uk

Self-Catering
C Hammond, Stourcliff Court, 56 Stourcliffe
Avenue, Southbourne, BOURNEMOUTH,
Dorset BH6 3PX Tel: 01202 420698
• website: www.stourcliffecourt.co.uk

Self-Catering
Lancombes House, West Milton, BRIDPORT,
Dorset DT6 3TN Tel: 01308 485375
• e-mail: info@lancombes-house.co.uk
• website: www.lancombes-house.co.uk

Caravan Park
Giants Head Caravan & Camping Park,
Old Sherborne Road, Cerne Abbas,
DORCHESTER, Dorset DT2 7TR
Tel: 01300 341242
• e-mail: holidays@giantshead.co.uk
• website: www.giantshead.co.uk

Farm / Self-Catering
Tamarisk Farm, West Bexington,
DORCHESTER, Dorset DT2 9DF
Tel: 01308 897784
• e-mail: holidays@tamariskfarm.com
• website: www.tamariskfarm.com

Hotel
Cromwell House Hotel, LULWORTH COVE,
Dorset BH20 5RJ
Tel: 01929 400253
• e-mail: catriona@lulworthcove.co.uk
• website: www.lulworthcove.co.uk

www.holidayguides.com

Self-Catering
Westover Farm Cottages, Wootton Fitzpaine,
Near LYME REGIS, Dorset DT6 6NE
Tel: 01297 560451/561395
• e-mail: wfcottages@aol.com
• website: www.westoverfarmcottages.co.uk

Farm / Self-Catering
White Horse Farm, Middlemarsh,
SHERBORNE, Dorset DT9 5QN
Tel: 01963 210222
• e-mail: enquiries@whitehorsefarm.co.uk
• website: www.whitehorsefarm.co.uk

Hotel
The Knoll House, STUDLAND BAY,
Dorset BH19 3AW Tel: 01929 450450
• e-mail: info@knollhouse.co.uk
• website: www.knollhouse.co.uk

Hotel
The Limes, 48 Park Road, SWANAGE,
Dorset BH19 2AE Tel: 01929 422664
• e-mail: info@limeshotel.net
• website: www.limeshotel.net

Farm/ Guest House/ Caravan & Camping
Luckford Wood House, East Stoke, Near
Lulworth, WAREHAM, Dorset BH20 6AW
Tel: 01929 463098/07888 719002
• e-mail: info@luckfordleisure.co.uk
• website: www.luckfordleisure.co.uk

Guest House/ Self-Catering
Glenthorne, Castle Cove, 15 Old Castle
Road, WEYMOUTH, Dorset DT4 8QB
Tel: 01305 777281
• e-mail: info@glenthorne-holidays.co.uk
• website: www.glenthorne-holidays.co.uk

•DURHAM

Self-Catering Cottages
Low Lands Farm, Lowlands, Cockfield,
BISHOP AUCKLAND, Durham DL13 5AW
Tel: 01388 718251
• e-mail: info@farmholidaysuk.com
• website: www.farmholidaysuk.com

Hotel
The Teesdale Hotel, MIDDLETON-IN-
TEESDALE, Durham DL12 0QG
Tel: 01833 640264
• e-mail: john@teesdalehotel.co.uk
• website: www.teesdalehotel.co.uk

•GLOUCESTERSHIRE

Hotel
Chester House Hotel, Victoria Street,
BOURTON-ON-THE-WATER,
Gloucs GL54 2BU Tel: 01451 820286
• e-mail: info@chesterhousehotel.com
• website: www.chesterhousehotel.com

Hotel
The Bowl Inn & Lilies Restaurant, 16 Church
Road, Lower Almondsbury, BRISTOL,
Gloucs BS32 4DT Tel: 01454 612757
• e-mail: reception@thebowlinn.co.uk
• website: www.thebowlinn.co.uk

Farmhouse B & B
Box Hedge Farm B & B, Box Hedge Farm
Lane, Coalpit Heath, BRISTOL,
Gloucs BS36 2UW Tel: 01454 250786
• e-mail: marilyn@bed-breakfast-bristol.com
• website: www.bed-breakfast-bristol.com

Hotel
Thornbury Golf Lodge, Bristol Road,
Thornbury, BRISTOL, Gloucs BS35 3XL
Tel: 01454 281144
• e-mail: info@thornburygc.co.uk
• website: www.thornburygc.co.uk

Self-Catering
Rose's Cottage, BROADWELL
Tel: 01451 830007
• e-mail: richard.drinkwater@ukonline.co.uk

B & B
Mrs C. Hutsby, Holly House, Ebrington,
CHIPPING CAMPDEN, Gloucs GL55 6NL
Tel: 01386 593213
• e-mail: hutsbybandb@aol.com
• website: www.hollyhousebandb.co.uk

Hotel
Tudor Farmhouse Hotel, CLEARWELL,
Forest of Dean, Gloucs GL16 8JS
Tel: 0800 7835935
• e-mail: info@tudorfarmhousehotel.co.uk
• website: www.tudorhousehotel.co.uk

Self-Catering
Wharton Lodge Cottages, FOREST OF
DEAN, Gloucs
Contact: Nicky Cross, Wharton Lodge
Cottages, Weston-Under-Penyard,
Herefordshire HR9 7JX Tel: 01989 750140
• e-mail: ncross@whartonlodge.co.uk
• website: www.whartonlodge.co.uk

B & B
Anthea & Bill Rhoton, Hyde Crest, Cirencester
Road, MINCHINHAMPTON, Gloucs GL6 8PE.
Tel: 01453 731631
• e-mail: stay@hydecrest.co.uk
• website: www.hydecrest.co.uk

•HAMPSHIRE

B & B
Mr & Mrs Farrell, Honeysuckle House,
24 Clinton Road, LYMINGTON,
Hampshire SO41 9EA Tel: 01590 676635
• e-mail: skyblue@beeb.net
• website:
http://explorethenewforest.co.uk/honeysuckle
.htm

Hotel
Crown Hotel, High Street, LYNDHURST,
Hampshire SO43 7NF Tel: 023 8028 2922
• e-mail: reception@crownhotel-lyndhurst.co.uk
• website: www.crownhotel-lyndhurst.co.uk

Hotel
Bramble Hill Hotel, Bramshaw,
Near LYNDHURST, New Forest,
Hampshire SO43 7JG Tel: 02380 813165
• website: www.bramblehill.co.uk

Caravan Park
Downton Holiday Park, Shorefield Road,
Milford-on-Sea, NEW FOREST,
Hampshire SO41 0LH
Tel: 01425 476131/01590 642515
• e-mail: info@downtonholidaypark.co.uk
• website: www.downtonholidaypark.co.uk

•HEREFORDSHIRE

Hotel
David & June Slade, Baskerville Arms Hotel,
Clyro, Near HAYE-ON-WYE, Herefordshire
HR3 5RZ Tel: 01497 820670
• e-mail: bookings@baskervillearms.co.uk
• website: www.baskervillearms.co.uk

Self-catering
The Rock Cottage, Huntington, KINGTON.
Contact: Mrs Williams, Radnor's End,
Huntington, KINGTON, Herefordshire
HR5 3NZ Tel: 01544 370289
• e-mail: enquires@the-rock-cottage.co.uk
• website: www.the-rock-cottage.co.uk

Farmhouse / B & B
Mrs M. E. Drzymalski, Thatch Close,
Llangrove, ROSS-ON-WYE, Herefordshire
HR9 6EL Tel: 01989 770300
• e-mail: info@thatchclose.co.uk
• website: www.thatchclose.co.uk

•KENT

Guest House
S. Twort, Heron Cottage, Biddenden,
ASHFORD, Kent TN27 8HH. Tel: 01580 291358
• e-mail: susantwort@hotmail.com
• website: www.heroncottage.info

Hotel
Collina House Hotel, 5 East Hill, TENTERDEN,
Kent TN30 6RL Tel: 01580 764852/764004
• e-mail: enquiries@collinahousehotel.co.uk
• website: www.collinahousehotel.co.uk

•LEICESTERSHIRE
& RUTLAND

Golf Club
Birstall Golf Club, Station Road, Birstall,
LEICESTER, Leicestershire LE4 3BB
Tel: 0116 267 4322
• e-mail: sue@birstallgolfclub.co.uk
• website: www.birstallgolfclub.co.uk

•LINCOLNSHIRE

Farm B & B / Self-catering cottage
Mrs C.E. Harrison, Baumber Park, Baumber,
HORNCASTLE, Lincolnshire LN9 5NE
Tel: 01507 578235/07977 722776
• e-mail: baumberpark@amserve.com
• website: www.baumberpark.com
        www.gathmanscottage.co.uk

Farmhouse B & B
S Evans, Willow Farm, Thorpe Fendykes,
SKEGNESS, Lincolnshire PE24 4QH
Tel: 01754 830316
• e-mail: willowfarmhols@aol.com
• website: www.willowfarmholidays.co.uk

Hotel
Petwood Hotel, Stixwood Road,
WOODHALL SPA, Lincolnshire LN10 6QF
Tel: 01526 352411
• e-mail: reception@petwood.co.uk
• website: www.petwood.co.uk

• MERSEYSIDE

Guest House
Holme Leigh Guest House, 93 Woodcroft
Road, Wavertree, LIVERPOOL,
Merseyside L15 2HG Tel: 0151 734 2216
• e-mail: info@holmeleigh.com
• website: www.holmeleigh.com

• NORFOLK

Self-Catering
Sand Dune Cottages, Tan Lane,
CAISTER-ON-SEA, Great Yarmouth,
Norfolk NR30 5DT Tel: 01493 720352
• e-mail: sand.dune.cottages@amserve.net
• website:
www.eastcoastlive.co.uk/sites/sanddunecottages.php

Self-catering
Scarning Dale, Dale Road, Scarning,
DEREHAM, Norfolk NR1 2QN
Tel: 01362 687269
• e-mail: jean@scarningdale.co.uk
• website: www.scarningdale.co.uk

Self-Catering
Idyllic Cottages at Vere Lodge,
South Raynham, FAKENHAM,
Norfolk NR21 7HE Tel: 01328 838261
• e-mail: major@verelodge.co.uk
• website: www.idylliccottages.co.uk

Self-Catering
Carefree Holidays, Chapel Briars, Yarmouth
Road, GREAT YARMOUTH, Norfolk NR29
4NJ Tel: 01493 732176
• e-mail: tony@carefree-holidays.co.uk
• website: www.carefree-holidays.co.uk

Self-Catering
Blue Riband Holidays, HEMSBY,
Great Yarmouth, Norfolk NR29 4HA
Tel: 01493 730445
• website: www.BlueRibandHolidays.co.uk

Hotel
The Stuart House Hotel, 35 Goodwins Road,
KING'S LYNN, Norfolk PE30 5QX
Tel: 01553 772169
• e-mail: reception@stuarthousehotel.co.uk
• website: www.stuarthousehotel.co.uk

B & B
Mrs J. Douglas, Greenacres Farm, Wood
Green, LONG STRATTON, Norwich, Norfolk
NR15 2RR Tel: 01508 530261
• website: www.abreakwithtradition.co.uk

B & B
Dolphin Lodge, 3 Knapton Road, Trunch,
NORTH WALSHAM, Norfolk NR28 0QE
Tel: 01263 720961
• e-mail: dolphin.lodge@btopenworld.com
• website: www.dolphinlodges.net

Self-Catering
Mr & Mrs Castleton, Poppyland Holiday
Cottages, The Green, THORPE MARKET,
Norfolk NR11 8AJ Tel: 01263 833219
• e-mail: poppylandjc@netscape.net
• website: www.poppyland.com

Self-Catering
Winterton Valley Holidays, WINTERTON-
ON-SEA/CALIFORNIA, Norfolk
Contact: 15 Kingston Avenue,Caister-on-
Sea NR30 5ET Tel: 01493 377175
• e-mail: info@wintertonvalleyholidays.co.uk
• website: www.wintertonvalleyholidays.co.uk

• NORTHUMBERLAND

Self-Catering
Buston Farm Holiday Cottages, ALNWICK,
Northumberland
Contact: Bygate, Black Heddon, Newcastle
Upon Tyne NE20 0JJ Tel: 01665 714805
• e-mail: stay@buston.co.uk
• website: www.buston.co.uk

Self-Catering
Heritage Coast Holidays, 6G Greensfield
Court, ALNWICK, Northumberland NE66
2DE
Tel: 01665 604935
• e-mail: info@heritagecoastholidays.com
• website: www.heritagecoastholidays.com

Self-Catering
Swinhoe Farm Cottages & Riding Centre,
Swinhoe Farmhouse, BELFORD,
Northumberland NE70 7LJ
Tel: 016682 13370
• e-mail: valerie@swinhoecottages.co.uk or
valerie.nixon@farming.co.uk
• website: www.swinhoecottages.co.uk

Hotel / Self-Catering
Riverdale Hall Hotel, BELLINGHAM,
Northumberland NE48 2JT
Tel: 01434 220254
• e-mail: reservations@riverdalehallhotel.co.uk
• website: www.riverdalehallhotel.co.uk

Hotel
The Cobbled Yard Hotel, 40 Walkergate,
BERWICK-UPON-TWEED, Northumberland
TD15 1DJ Tel: 01289 308407
• e-mail:
cobbledyardhotel@berwick35.fsnet.co.uk
• website: www.cobbledyardhotel.com

B & B / Farm / Camping
Mrs S. Maughan, Greencarts Farm, Near
Humshaugh, HEXHAM, Northumberland
NE46 4BW Tel: 01434 681320
• e-mail: sandra@greencarts.co.uk
• website: www.greencarts.co.uk

Self-Catering
Burradon Farm Cottages & Houses,
Burradon Farm, Cramlington, NEWCASTLE-
UPON-TYNE, Northumberland NE23 7ND
Tel: 0191 2683203
• e-mail: judy@burradonfarm.co.uk
• website: www.burradonfarm.co.uk

Golf Club
Seahouses Golf Club, Beadnell Road,
SEAHOUSES, Northumberland NE67 7XT
Tel: 01665 720794
• e-mail: secretary@seahousesgolf.co.uk
• website: www.seahousesgolf.co.uk

Guest House / B & B
Mrs M. Halliday, Beck'n'Call, Birling West
Cottage, WARKWORTH, Northumberland
NE65 0XS Tel: 01665 711653
• e-mail: beck-n-call@lineone.net
• website: www.beck-n-call.co.uk

•OXFORDSHIRE

Leisure Park
Cotswold Wildlife Park, BURFORD,
Oxfordshire OX18 4JN Tel: 01993 823006
• website: www.cotswoldwildlifepark.co.uk

B & B
The Old Bakery, Skirmett, Near HENLEY-ON-
THAMES, Oxfordshire RG9 6TD
Tel: 01491 410716
• e-mail: lizzroach@aol.com

Guest House
The Bungalow, Cherwell Farm, Mill Lane,
Old Marston, OXFORD,
Oxfordshire OX3 0QF Tel: 01865 557171
• e-mail: ros.bungalowbb@btinternet.com
• www.cherwellfarm-oxford-accomm.co.uk

Guest House
Nanford Guest House, 137 Iffley Road,
OXFORD, Oxfordshire, OX4 1EJ
Tel: 01865 244743
• e-mail: b.cronin@btinternet.com
• website: www.nanfordguesthouse.com

B & B / Self-Catering
Katharine Brown, Hill Grove Farm, Crawley
Dry Lane, Minster Lovell, WITNEY,
Oxfordshire OX29 0NA Tel: 01993 703120
• e-mail: katharinemcbrown@btinternet.com
• website:
www.countryaccom.co.uk/hill-grove-farm

•SHROPSHIRE

Farm / B & B
Mrs Mary Jones, Acton Scott Farm, Acton
Scott, CHURCH STRETTON, Shropshire
SY6 6QN Tel: 01694 781260
• e-mail: fhg@actonscottfarm.co.uk
• website: www.actonscottfarm.co.uk

Self-Catering
Clive & Cynthia Prior, Mocktree Barns
Holiday Cottages, Leintwardine, LUDLOW,
Shropshire SY7 0LY Tel: 01547 540441
• e-mail: mocktreebarns@care4free.net
• website: www.mocktreeholidays.co.uk

Inn / Hotel

The Four Alls Inn, Woodseaves,
MARKET DRAYTON, Shropshire TF9 2AG
Tel: 01630 652995
• e-mail: inn@thefouralls.com
• website: www.thefouralls.com

Hotel

M. Hunter, Pen-Y-Dyffryn Hotel,
Rhydycroseau, OSWESTRY, Shropshire
SY10 7JD Tel: 01691 653700
• e-mail: stay@peny.co.uk
• website: www.peny.co.uk

•SOMERSET

B&B

Mrs C. Bryson, Walton Villa, 3 Newbridge
Hill, BATH, Somerset BA1 3PW
Tel: 01225 482792
•e-mail: walton.villa@virgin.net
•website: www.waltonvilla.com

Inn

The Talbot 15th Century Coaching Inn,
Selwood Street, Mells, Near BATH,
Somerset BA11 3PN Tel: 01373 812254
• e-mail: roger@talbotinn.com
• website: www.talbotinn.com

Farm Guest House / Self-Catering

Jackie & David Bishop, Toghill House Farm,
Freezing Hill, Wick, Near BATH,
Somerset BS30 5RT. Tel: 01225 891261
• e-mail:
accommodation@toghillhousefarm.co.uk
• website: www.toghillhousefarm.co.uk

Self-Catering

Westward Rise Holiday Park, South Road,
BREAN, Burnham-on-Sea, Somerset
TA8 2RD Tel: 01278 751310
• e-mail: info@westwardrise.com
• website: www.westwardrise.com

Farm / B & B

Mrs M. Hasell, The Model Farm, Norton
Hawkfield, Pensford, BRISTOL, Somerset
BS39 4HA Tel: 01275 832144
• e-mail: margarethasell@hotmail.com
• website: www.themodelfarm.co.uk

Farmhouse / Self-Catering

Josephine Smart, Leigh Farm, Old Road,
Pensford, NEAR BRISTOL, Somerset
BS39 4BA Tel: 01761 490281
• website: www.leighfarm.co.uk

Self-Catering Cottages

Mrs E. M. Neville, Wood Dairy, Wood Lane,
North Perrott, Near CREWKERNE, Somerset
TA18 7TA Tel: 01935 891532
• e-mail: liz@acountryretreat.co.uk
• website: www.acountryretreat.co.uk

Self-Catering

The Pack Horse, Allerford, Near Porlock,
EXMOOR, Somerset TA24 8HW
Tel: 01643 862475
• e-mail: holidays@thepackhorse.net
• website: www.thepackhorse.net

Farm Self-Catering & Camping

Westermill Farm, Exford, EXMOOR,
Somerset TA24 7NJ
Tel: 01643 831238
• e-mail: fhg@westermill.com
• website: www.westermill.com

Farm Self-Catering

Jane Styles, Wintershead Farm,
Simonsbath, EXMOOR, Somerset TA24 7LF
Tel: 01643 831222
• e-mail: wintershead@yahoo.co.uk
• website: www.wintershead.co.uk

B & B / Half-Board / Self-Catering / Towing Pitches

St Audries Bay Holiday Club, West
Quantoxhead, MINEHEAD, Somerset
TA4 4DY Tel: 01984 632515
• e-mail: info@staudriesbay.co.uk
• website: www.staudriesbay.co.uk

Guest House

The Old Mill, Netherclay, Bishop's Hull,
TAUNTON, Somerset TA1 5AB
Tel: 01823 289732
• website: www.theoldmillbandb.co.uk

B & B

North Down Farm, Pyncombe Lane,
Wiveliscombe, TAUNTON, Somerset TA4
2BL Tel: 01984 623730
• e-mail: jennycope@btinternet.com
• website: north-down-farm.co.uk

B & B

G. Clark, Yew Tree Farm, THEALE,
Near Wedmore, Somerset BS28 4SN
Tel: 01934 712475
• e-mail: enquiries@yewtreefarmbandb.co.uk
• website: www.yewtreefarmbandb.co.uk

Self-Catering

Croft Holiday Cottages, 2 The Croft, Anchor
Street, WATCHET, Somerset TA23 0BY
Tel: 01984 631121
• e-mail: croftcottages@talk21.com
• website: www.cottagessomerset.com

Guest House
Infield House, 36 Portway, WELLS,
Somerset BA5 2BN Tel: 01749 670989
• e-mail: infield@talk21.com
• website: www.infieldhouse.co.uk

B & B
Susan Crane, Birdwood House, Bath Road,
WELLS, Somerset BA5 3EW
Tel: 01749 679250
• e-mail: susancrane@mb2online.net
• website: www.birdwood-bandb.co.uk

Self-Catering / B & B
Mrs C. Glass, Islington Farm, WELLS,
Somerset BA5 1US Tel: 01749 673445
• e-mail: islingtonfarm2004@yahoo.co.uk
• website: www.islingtonfarmatwells.co.uk

Caravan Park
Ardnave Holiday Park, Kewstoke, WESTON-
SUPER-MARE, Somerset BS22 9XJ
Tel: 01934 622319
• website: www.ardnaveholidaypark.co.uk

Guest House
Julie Bridgeman, Sunset Bay Hotel, 53
Beach Road, WESTON-SUPER-MARE,
Somerset BS23 1BH Tel: 01934 623519
• e-mail: relax@sunsetbayhotel.co.uk
• website: www.sunsetbayhotel.co.uk

•STAFFORDSHIRE

Farm B & B / Self-Catering
Mrs M. Hiscoe-James, Offley Grove Farm,
Adbaston, ECCLESHALL, Staffordshire
ST20 0QB. Tel: 01785 280205
• e-mail: enquiries@offleygrovefarm.co.uk
• website: www.offleygrovefarm.co.uk

•SUFFOLK

Guest House
Dunston Guest House, 8 Springfield Road,
BURY ST EDMUNDS, Suffolk IP33 3AN
Tel: 01284 764574
• website: www.dunstonguesthouse.co.uk

B & B
Kay Dewsbury, Manorhouse, The Green,
Beyton, BURY ST EDMUNDS, Suffolk IP30 9AF
Tel: 01359 270960
• e-mail: manorhouse@beyton.com
• website: www.beyton.com

Hotel
Ravenwood Hall Country House Hotel &
Restaurant, Rougham,
BURY ST EDMUNDS, Suffolk IP30 9JA
Tel: 01359 270345
• e-mail: enquiries@ravenwoodhall.co.uk
• website: www.ravenwoodhall.co.uk

Guest House
The Grafton Guest House, 13 Sea Road,
FELIXSTOWE, Suffolk IP11 2BB
Tel: 01394 284881
• e-mail: info@grafton-house.com
• website: www.grafton-house.com

B & B / Self-Catering
Mrs Sarah Kindred, High House Farm,
Cransford, Woodbridge, FRAMLINGHAM,
Suffolk IP13 9PD Tel: 01728 663461
• e-mail: b&b@highhousefarm.co.uk
• website: www.highhousefarm.co.uk

Self-Catering
Kessingland Cottages, Rider Haggard Lane,
KESSINGLAND, Suffolk.
Contact: S. Mahmood,
156 Bromley Road, Beckenham,
Kent BR3 6PG Tel: 020 8650 0539
• e-mail: jeeptrek@kjti.co.uk
• website: www.k-cottage.co.uk

Hotel
The Black Lion Hotel & Restaurant,
The Green, LONG MELFORD, Suffolk
CO10 9DN Tel: 01787 312356
• e-mail: enquiries@blacklionhotel.net
• website: www.blacklionhotel.net

Self-Catering
Southwold/Walberswick Self-Catering
Properties.
Durrants incorporating, H.A. Adnams, 98
High Street, SOUTHWOLD, Suffolk
IP18 6DP Tel: 01502 723292
• website: www.durrants.com

Self-Catering
Windmill Lodges Ltd, Redhouse Farm,
Saxtead, WOODBRIDGE, Suffolk IP13 9RD
Tel: 01728 685338
• e-mail: holidays@windmilllodges.co.uk
• website: www.windmilllodges.co.uk

Readers are requested to mention this FHG
guidebook when seeking accommodation

•EAST SUSSEX

Self-Catering
Crowhurst Park, Telham Lane, BATTLE, East Sussex TN33 0SL Tel: 01424 773344
• e-mail: enquiries@crowhurstpark.co.uk
• website: www.crowhurstpark.co.uk

Hotel / B & B
Maon Hotel, 26 Upper Rock Gardens, BRIGHTON, East Sussex BN2 1QE
Tel: 01273 694400
• e-mail: maonhotel@aol.com
• website: www.maonhotel.co.uk

Self- Catering
Kilcolgan Premier Bungalows, Rottingdean Seaside Village, BRIGHTON, East Sussex BN2 7DL
Contact: J. C. St George, 22 Baches Street, London N1 6DL Tel: 020 7250 3678
• e-mail: jc.stgeorge@virgin.net
• website: www.holidaybungalowsbrightonuk.com

Self-Catering
"Pekes", CHIDDINGLY, East Sussex
Contact: Eva Morris, 124 Elm Park Mansions, Park Walk, London SW10 0AR
Tel: 020 7352 8088
• e-mail: pekes.afa@virgin.net
• website: www.pekesmanor.com

Guest House / Self-Catering
Longleys Farm Cottage, Harebeating Lane, HAILSHAM, East Sussex BN27 1ER
Tel: 01323 841227
• e-mail: longleysfarmcottagebb@dsl.pipex.com
• website: www.longleysfarmcottage.co.uk

Hotel
Grand Hotel, Grand Parade, St. Leonards, HASTINGS, East Sussex TN38 0DD
Tel: 01424 428510
• e-mail: info@grandhotelhastings.co.uk
• website: www.grandhotelhastings.co.uk

Hotel
Jeake's House, Mermaid Street, RYE, East Sussex TN31 7ET
Tel: 01797 222828
• e-mail: stay@jeakeshouse.com
• website: www.jeakeshouse.com

Hotel
Flackley Ash Hotel & Restaurant, Peasmarsh, Near RYE, East Sussex TN31 6YH. Tel: 01797 230651
• e-mail: enquiries@flackleyashhotel.co.uk
• website: www.flackleyashhotel.co.uk

Self-Catering Cottage
4 Beach Cottages, Claremont Road, SEAFORD, East Sussex BN25 2QQ
Contact: Julia Lewis, 47 Wandle Bank, London SW19 1DW Tel: 020 8542 5073
• e-mail: cottage@beachcottages.info
• website: www.beachcottages.info

• WEST SUSSEX

B & B
Mrs Vicki Richards, Woodacre, Arundel Road, Fontwell, ARUNDEL, West Sussex BN18 0QP Tel: 01243 814301
• e-mail: wacrebb@aol.com
• website: www.woodacre.co.uk

Self-Catering
Honeybridge Park, Honeybridge Lane, DIAL POST, Horsham, West Sussex RH13 8NX
Tel: 01403 710923
• e-mail: enquiries@honeybridgepark.co.uk
• website: www.honeybridgepark.co.uk

B & B
Broxmead Paddock, Broxmead Lane, Bolney, HAYWARDS HEATH, West Sussex RH17 5RG
Tel: 01444 881458
• e-mail: broxmeadpaddock@hotmail.com
• website: www.broxmeadpaddock.eclipse.co.uk

Self-Catering
Mrs M. W. Carreck, New Hall Holiday Flat and Cottage, New Hall Lane, Small Dole, HENFIELD, West Sussex BN5 9YJ
Tel: 01273 492546
• website: www.newhallcottage.co.uk

•WARWICKSHIRE

Guest House / B & B
Julia & John Downie, Holly Tree Cottage, Pathlow, STRATFORD-UPON-AVON, Warwickshire CV37 0ES Tel: 01789 204461
• e-mail: john@hollytree-cottage.co.uk
• website: www.hollytree-cottage.co.uk

Caravan Park
Riverside Caravan Park, Tiddington Road, STRATFORD-UPON-AVON, Warwickshire CV37 7AB Tel: 01789 292312
• website: www.stratfordcaravans.co.uk

•WEST MIDLANDS

Hotel / Self-catering
Featherstone Farm Hotel, New Road,
Featherstone, WOLVERHAMPTON, West
Midlands WV10 7NW Tel: 01902 725371
- e-mail: info@featherstonefarm.co.uk
- website: www.featherstonefarm.co.uk

•WILTSHIRE

Guest House
Alan & Dawn Curnow, Hayburn Wyke
Guest House, 72 Castle Road, SALISBURY,
Wiltshire SP1 3RL Tel:01722 412627
- e-mail: hayburn.wyke@tinyonline.co.uk
- website: www.hayburnwykeguesthouse.co.uk

Golf Club
High Post Golf Club, High Post, SALISBURY,
Wiltshire SP4 6AT Tel: 01722 782219
- e-mail: secretary@highpostgolfclub.co.uk
- website: www.highpostgolfclub.co.uk

Self-Catering Cottage
Manor Farm Cottages, Manor Farm, Sutton
Mandeville, SALISBURY, Wiltshire SP3 5NL
Tel: 01722 714226
- e-mail: strangf@aol.com
- website: www.strangcottages.com

Golf Club
Wrag Barn Golf & Country Club, Shrivenham
Road, High Worth, SWINDON, Wiltshire
SN6 7QQ Tel: 01793 861327
- e-mail: manager@wragbarn.com
- website: www.wragbarn.co.uk

Golf Club
West Wilts Golf Club, Elm Hill,
WARMINSTER, Wiltshire BA12 0AU
Tel: 01985 213133
- e-mail: sec@westwiltsgolfclub.co.uk
- website: www.westwiltsgolfclub.co.uk

•WORCESTERSHIRE

B & B / Self-Catering
Mrs Tricia Havard, Phepson Farm,
Himbleton, DROITWICH, Worcestershire
WR9 7J2 Tel: 01905 391205
- e-mail: havard@globalnet.co.uk
- website: www.phepsonfarm.co.uk

Guest House
Ann & Brian Porter, Croft Guest House,
Bransford, GREAT MALVERN, Worcester,
Worcestershire WR6 5JD Tel: 01886 832227
- e-mail: hols@crofthousewr6.fsnet.co.uk
- website: www.croftguesthouse.com

Self-Catering Cottages
Rochford Park, TENBURY WELLS,
Worcestershire WR15 8SP
Tel: 01584 781 372
- e-mail: cottages@rochfordpark.co.uk
- website: www.rochfordpark.co.uk

Inn
The Manor Arms At Abberley, The Village,
Abberley, WORCESTER, Worcestershire
WR6 6BH Tel: 01299 896507
- e-mail: info@themanorarms.co.uk
- website: www.themanorarms.co.uk

•EAST YORKSHIRE

Self-Catering
Chris Wade, Waterfront Cottages, 2 Star
Row, NORTH DALTON, Driffield, East
Yorkshire YO25 9UX Tel: 01377 217662
- e-mail: chris.wade@adastra-music.co.uk
- www.waterfrontcottages.co.uk

Guest House / Camping
Mrs Jeanne Wilson, Robeanne House,
Driffield Lane, Shiptonthorpe, YORK, East
Yorkshire YO43 3PW Tel: 01430 873312
- e-mail: enquiries@robeannehouse.co.uk
- website: www.robeannehouse.co.uk

•NORTH YORKSHIRE

Self-Catering
Recommended Cottage Holidays, Eastgate
House, Pickering, NORTH YORKSHIRE
Tel: 01751 475547
- website: www.recommended-cottages.co.uk

Farmhouse B & B
Mrs Julie Clarke, Middle Farm, Woodale,
COVERDALE, Leyburn,
North Yorkshire DL8 4TY Tel: 01969 640271
- e-mail: j-a-clarke@hotmail.co.uk
- www.yorkshirenet.co.uk/stayat/middlefarm

Farm
Mrs Linda Tindall, Rowantree Farm, Fryup
Road, Ainthorpe, DANBY, Whitby,
North Yorkshire YO21 2LE
Tel: 01723 515155
- e-mail: krbsatindall@aol.com
- website: www.rowantreefarm.co.uk

Farmhouse B&B

Mr & Mrs Richardson, Egton Banks Farmhouse, GLAISDALE, Whitby, North Yorkshire YO21 2QP Tel: 01947 897289
- e-mail: egtonbanksfarm@agriplus.net
- website: www.egtonbanksfarm.agriplus.net

Caravan & Camping

Bainbridge Ings Caravan & Camping Site, HAWES, North Yorkshire DL8 3NU Tel: 01969 667354
- e-mail: janet@bainbridge-ings.co.uk
- website: www.bainbridge-ings.co.uk

Guest House

The New Inn Motel, Main Street, HUBY, York, North Yorkshire YO61 1HQ Tel: 01347 810219
- enquiries@newinnmotel.freeserve.co.uk
- website: www.newinnmotel.co.uk

Hotel

Anne Wood, Golden Lion Hotel, Market Square, LEYBURN, North Yorkshire DL8 5AS Tel: 01969 622161
- e-mail: info@goldenlionleyburn.co.uk
- website: www.goldenlionleyburn.co.uk

Self-Catering

Mrs L. J. Story, Holmes Farm Cottage, Holmes Farm, LOW BENTHAM, Lancaster LA2 7DE Tel: 01524 261198
- e-mail: lucy@holmesfarmcottage.co.uk
- website: www.holmesfarmcottage.co.uk

Self-Catering

Abbey Holiday Cottages, MIDDLESMOOR. 12 Panorama Close, Pateley Bridge, Harrogate, North Yorkshire HG3 5NY Tel: 01423 712062
- e-mail: info@abbeyhall.cottages.co.uk
- website: www.abbeyholidaycottages.co.uk

B & B

Banavie, Roxby Road, Thornton-Le-Dale, PICKERING, North Yorkshire YO18 7SX Tel: 01751 474616
- e-mail: info@banavie.co.uk
- website: www.banavie.uk.com

Guest House / Self-Catering

Sue & Tony Hewitt, Harmony Country Lodge, 80 Limestone Road, Burniston, SCARBOROUGH, North Yorkshire YO13 0DG Tel: 0800 2985840
- e-mail: mail@harmonylodge.net
- website: www.harmonylodge.net

B & B

Beck Hall, Malham, SKIPTON, North Yorkshire BD23 4DJ Tel: 01729 830332
- e-mail: simon@beckhallmalham.com
- website: www.beckhallmalham.com

Inn

Gamekeepers Inn, Long Ashes Park, Threshfield, NEAR SKIPTON, North Yorkshire BD23 5PN Tel: 01756 752434
- e-mail: info@gamekeeperinn.co.uk
- website: www.gamekeeperinn.co.uk

Self-Catering

Mrs Jones, New Close Farm, Kirkby Malham, SKIPTON, North Yorkshire BD23 4DP Tel: 01729 830240
- brendajones@newclosefarmyorkshire.co.uk
- website: www.newclosefarmyorkshire.co.uk

Self-Catering

Pennystell Cottage, 3 Boathouse Yard, STAITHES, North Yorkshire TS13 5BN
Contact: Chris Wade, 2 Star Row, Driffield, East Yorkshire YO25 9UX Tel: 01377 217662
- e-mail: chris.wade@adastra-music.co.uk
- www.waterfrontcottages.co.uk

Guest House

Ashford Guest House, 8 Royal Crescent, WHITBY, North Yorkshire YO21 3EJ Tel: 01947 602138
- e-mail: info@ashfordguesthouse.co.uk
- website: www.ashfordguesthouse.co.uk

Self-Catering

Greenhouses Farm Cottages, Near WHITBY. Contact: Mr J.N. Eddleston, Thistledown Cottage. Greenhouses Farm, Lealholm, North Yorkshire YO21 2AD Tel: 01947 897486
- e-mail: n_eddleston@yahoo.com
- www.greenhouses-farm-cottages.co.uk

Hotel

Blossoms Hotel York, 28 Clifden, YORK, North Yorkshire YO3 6AE Tel: 01904 652391
- e-mail: fhg@blossomsyork.co.uk
- website: www.blossomsyork.co.uk

B & B

Mrs Butterworth, Wellgarth House, Wetherby Road, Rufforth, YORK, North Yorkshire YO23 3QB Tel: 01904 738592
- e-mail: enquiries@wellgarthhouse.co.uk
- website: wellgarthhouse.co.uk

•WEST YORKSHIRE

B & B / Self-Catering Cottages

Currer Laithe Farm, Moss Carr Road, Long Lee, KEIGHLEY, West Yorkshire BD21 4SL Tel: 01535 604387
- website: www.currerlaithe.co.uk

•SCOTLAND

Self-Catering Cottages
Islands & Highlands Cottages, Bridge Road,
Portree, Isle of Skye, SCOTLAND IV51 9ER
Tel: 01478 612123
• website: www.islands-and-highlands.co.uk

•ABERDEEN, BANFF & MORAY

Hotel
P. A. McKechnie, Cambus O' May Hotel,
BALLATER, Aberdeenshire AB35 5SE
Tel: 013397 55428
• e-mail:
mckechnie@cambusomay.freeserve.co.uk
• website: www.cambusomayhotel.co.uk

B & B
Davaar B & B, Church Street, DUFFTOWN,
Moray, AB55 4AR Tel: 01340 820464
• e-mail: davaar@cluniecameron.co.uk
• website: www.davaardufftown.co.uk

Self-catering
Newseat & Kirklea, FRASERBURGH,
Aberdeenshire.
Contact: Mrs E.M. Pittendrigh, Kirktown, Tyrie,
Fraserburgh, Aberdeenshire AB43 7DQ.
Tel: 01346 541231
•e-mail: pittendrigh@supanet.com

Self-Catering
The Greenknowe, INVERURIE.
Contact: Kingsfield House, Kingsfield Road,
Kintore, Inverurie, Aberdeenshire AB51 0UD
Tel: 01467 632366
• e-mail: info@holidayhomesaberdeen.com
• website: www.holidayhomesaberdeen.com

Golf Club
Moray Golf Club, Stotfield Road,
LOSSIEMOUTH, Moray IV31 6QS
Tel: 01343 812018
• e-mail: secretary@moraygolf.co.uk
• website: www.moraygolf.co.uk

•ANGUS & DUNDEE

Golf Club
Edzell Golf Club, High Street, EDZELL,
Brechin, Angus DD9 7TF
Tel: 01356 648462
• e-mail: secretary@edzellgolfclub.net
• website: www.edzellgolfclub.net

Golf Club
Forfar Golf Club, Cunninghill, Arbroath
Road, FORFAR, Angus DD8 2RL
Tel: 01307 463773
• e-mail: info@forfargolfclub.com
• website: www.forfargolfclub.com

•ARGYLL & BUTE

Self-Catering / Touring Park
Resipole Farm Camping & Caravan Park,
Loch Sunart, ACHARACLE, Argyll PH36 4HX
Tel: 01967 431235
• e-mail: info@resipole.co.uk
• website: www.resipole.co.uk

Self-Catering
Ardtur Cottages, APPIN, Argyll PA38 4DD
Tel: 01631 730223
• e-mail: pery@btinternet.com
• website: www.selfcatering-appin-scotland.com

Inn
Mr D. Fraser, Cairndow Stagecoach Inn,
CAIRNDOW, Argyll PA26 8BN
Tel: 01499 600286
• e-mail: cairndowinn@aol.com
• website: www.cairndow.com

Golf Club
The Machrihanish Golf Club, Machrihanish,
CAMPBELTOWN, Argyll PA28 6PT
Tel: 01586 810213
• e-mail: secretary@machgolf.com
• website: www.machgolf.com

Guest House / Self-Catering
Rockhill Waterside Country House,
DALMALLY, Argyll PA33 1BH
Tel: 01866 833218
• website: www.rockhillfarmguesthouse.co.uk

Self-Catering
Mrs I. Crawford, Blarghour Farm Cottages,
Blarghour Farm, By DALMALLY,
Argyll PA33 1BW Tel: 01866 833246
• e-mail: blarghour@btconnect.com
• website: www.self-catering-argyll.co.uk

Self-catering
Kilbride Croft, Balvicar, ISLE OF SEIL, Argyll
PA34 4RD Tel: 01852 300475
• e-mail: kilbridecroft@aol.com
• website: www.kilbridecroft.co.uk

Caravans
Caolasnacon Caravan Park, KINLOCHLEVEN,
Argyll PH50 4RJ Tel: 01855 831279
• website: www.kinlochlevencaravans.com

Self-Catering
Inchmurrin Island Self-Catering Holidays,
Inchmurrin Island, LOCH LOMOND
G63 0JY Tel: 01389 850245
• e-mail: scotts@inchmurrin-lochlomond.com
• website: www.inchmurrin-lochlomond.com

Self-Catering
Linda Battison,
Cologin Country Chalets & Lodges,
Lerags Glen, OBAN, Argyll PA34 4SE
Tel: 01631 564501
• e-mail: info@cologin.co.uk
• website: www.west-highland-holidays.co.uk

Self-Catering
Colin Mossman, Lagnakeil Lodges,
Lerags, OBAN, Argyll PA34 4SE
Tel: 01631 562746
• e-mail: info@lagnakeil.co.uk
• website: www.lagnakeil.co.uk

Self-Catering
Mrs Barker, Barfad Farm, TARBERT,
Loch Fyne, Argyll PA29 6YH
Tel: 01880 820549
• e-mail: vbarker@hotmail.com
• website: www.tarbertlochfyne.com

•AYRSHIRE & ARRAN

B & B
Mrs J Clark, Eglinton Guest House,
23 Eglinton Terrace, AYR, Ayrshire KA7 1JJ
Tel: 01292 264623
• e-mail: eglintonguesthouse@yahoo.co.uk
• website: www.eglinton-guesthouse-ayr.com

Hotel
Catacol Bay Hotel, CATACOL, Lochranza,
Isle of Arran KA27 8HN
Tel: 01770 830231
• e-mail: catbay@tiscali.co.uk
• website: www.catacol.co.uk

Farmhouse / B & B
Mrs Nancy Cuthbertson, West Tannacrieff,
Fenwick, KILMARNOCK, Ayrshire KA3 6AZ
Tel: 01560 600258
• e-mail: westtannacrieff@btopenworld.com
• website: www.smoothhound.co.uk/hotels/
westtannacrieff.html

Farmhouse / B & B / Caravan & Camping
Mrs M Watson, South Whittlieburn Farm,
Brisbane Glen, LARGS, Ayrshire KA30 8SN
Tel: 01475 675881
• e-mail:
largsbandb@southwhittlieburnfarm.freeserve.co.uk
• website: www.ukcampsite.co.uk
www.smoothhound.co.uk/hotels/whittlie.html

•BORDERS

Guest House
Ferniehirst Mill Lodge, JEDBURGH,
Borders TD8 6PQ Tel: 01835 863279
• e-mail: ferniehirstmill@aol.com
• website: www.ferniehirstmill.co.uk

Self-Catering
Mill House, JEDBURGH.
Contact: Mrs A. Fraser, Overwells,
Jedburgh, Borders TD8 6LT
Tel: 01835 863020
• e-mail: abfraser@btinternet.com
• website: www.overwells.co.uk

Self-Catering
Mrs C. M. Kilpatrick, Slipperfield House,
WEST LINTON, Peeblesshire EH46 7AA
Tel: 01968 660401
• e-mail: cottages@slipperfield.com
• website: www.slipperfield.com

•DUMFRIES & GALLOWAY

Self-Catering
Cloud Cuckoo Lodge, CASTLE DOUGLAS,
Dumfries & Galloway
Contact: Mrs Lesley Wykes, Cuckoostone
Cottage, St John's Town Of Dalry, Castle
Douglas DG7 3UA Tel: 01644 430375
• e-mail: enquiries@cloudcuckoolodge.co.uk
• website: www.cloudcuckoolodge.co.uk

Guest House
Celia Pickup, Craigadam,
CASTLE DOUGLAS, Kirkcudbrightshire
DG7 3HU Tel: 01556 650233
• website: www.craigadam.com

Self-Catering
Ae Farm Cottages, Gubhill Farm,
DUMFRIES, Dumfriesshire DG1 1RL
Tel: 01387 860648
•e-mail: gill@gubhill.co.uk
•website: www.aefarmcottages.co.uk

B & B
Langlands Bed & Breakfast, 8 Edinburgh
Road, DUMFRIES, Dumfries & Galloway
DG1 1JQ Tel: 01387 266549
• e-mail: langlands@tiscali.co.uk
•website: www.langlands.info

Farm / Camping & Caravans / Self-Catering
Barnsoul Farm Holidays, Barnsoul Farm,
Shawhead, DUMFRIES, Dumfriesshire
Tel: 01387 730249
• e-mail: barnsouldg@aol.com
• website: www.barnsoulfarm.co.uk

Self-Catering
Rusko Holidays, GATEHOUSE OF FLEET,
Castle Douglas, Kirkcudbrightshire
DG7 2BS Tel: 01557 814215
• e-mail: info@ruskoholidays.co.uk
• website: www.ruskoholidays.co.uk

Self-Catering
G & S Cottages, PORTPATRICK,
Dumfries & Galloway
Contact: Graham & Sue Fletcher, 468 Otley
Road, Leeds, Yorkshire LS16 8AE
Tel: 0113 2301391
• e-mail: info@gscottages.co.uk
• website: www.gscottages.co.uk

•EDINBURGH & LOTHIANS

Guest House
Kenvie Guest House, 16 Kilmaurs Road,
EDINBURGH EH16 5DA Tel: 0131 6681964
•e-mail: dorothy@kenvie.co.uk
• website: www.kenvie.co.uk

Guest House
International Guest House, 37 Mayfield
Gardens, EDINBURGH EH9 2BX
Tel: 0131 667 2511
• e-mail: intergh1@yahoo.co.uk
• website: www.accommodation-edinburgh.com

•HIGHLANDS

Self-Catering
Mr M W MacLeod, Dornie House Chalets,
Dornie House, ACHILTIBUIE, By Ullapool,
Ross-shire IV26 2YP Tel: 01854 622271
• e-mail: dorniehousebandb@aol.com

Self-Catering
Cairngorm Highland Bungalows,
AVIEMORE.
Contact: Linda Murray, 29 Grampian View,
Aviemore, Inverness-shire PH22 1TF
Tel: 01479 810653
• e-mail: linda.murray@virgin.net
• website: www.cairngorm-bungalows.co.uk

Self Catering / Caravans
Speyside Leisure Park, Dalfaber Road,
AVIEMORE, Inverness-shire PH22 1PX
Tel: 01479 810236
• e-mail: fhg@speysideleisure.com
• website: www.speysideleisure.com

Luxury Self-Catering
Crubenbeg Highland Holiday Cottages,
Near AVIEMORE, Highlands PH20 1BE
Tel: 01540 673566
• e-mail: enquiry@highlandholidaycottages.com
• website: www.highlandholidaycottages.com

Hotel / Self-Catering
Royal Marine Hotel & Leisure Club, Golf
Road, BRORA, Sutherland KW9 6QS
Tel: 01408 621252
• e-mail: info@highlandescape.com
• website: www.highlandescapehotels.com

Guest House
Mrs Lynn Benge, The Pines Country House,
Duthil, CARRBRIDGE, Inverness-shire
PH23 3ND Tel: 01479 841220
• e-mail: lynn@thepines-duthil.co.uk
• website: www.thepines-duthil.co.uk

Golf Club
The Royal Dornoch Golf Club, Golf Road,
DORNOCH, Sutherland IV25 3LW
Tel: 01862 810219 Ext 185
• e-mail: bookings@royaldornoch.com
• website: www.royaldornoch.com

Self-Catering
Carol Hughes, Glenurquhart Lodges,
Balnain, DRUMNADROCHIT, Inverness-shire
IV63 6TJ Tel: 01456 476234
• e-mail: info@glenurquhart-lodges.co.uk
• website: www.glenurquhart-lodges.co.uk

Hotel
The Clan MacDuff Hotel, Achintore Road,
FORT WILLIAM, Inverness-shire PH33 6RW
Tel: 01397 702341
• e-mail: reception@clanmacduff.co.uk
• website: www.clanmacduff.co.uk

Caravan & Camping
Auchnahillin Caravan & Camping Park,
Daviot East, INVERNESS, Inverness-shire
IV2 5XQ Tel: 01463 772286
• e-mail: info@auchnahillin.co.uk
• website: www.auchnahillin.co.uk

Self-Catering
Wildside Highland Lodges, Whitebridge,
By LOCH NESS, Inverness-shire IV2 6UN
Tel: 01456 486373
• e-mail: info@wildsidelodges.com
• website: www.wildsidelodges.com

B & B / Self-Catering Chalets
D.J. Mordaunt, Mondhuie, NETHY BRIDGE,
Inverness-shire PH25 3DF Tel: 01479 821062
• e-mail: david@mondhuie.com
• website: www.mondhuie.com

Hotel
Kintail Lodge Hotel, SHIEL BRIDGE,
Glenshiel, Ross-shire IV40 8HL
Tel: 01599 511275
• e-mail: kintaillodgehotel@btinternet.com
• website: www.kintaillodgehotel.co.uk

Hotel / Sporting Lodge
Borgie Lodge Hotel, SKERRAY, Sutherland
KW14 7TH Tel: 01641 521332
• e-mail: info@borgielodgehotel.co.uk
• website: www.borgielodgehotel.co.uk

Hotel
Whitebridge Hotel, WHITEBRIDGE,
Inverness IV2 6UN Tel: 01456 486226
• e-mail: info@whitebridgehotel.co.uk
• website: www.whitebridgehotel.co.uk

•LANARKSHIRE

Caravan & Holiday Home Park
Mount View Caravan Park, Station Road,
ABINGTON, South Lanarkshire ML12 6RW
Tel: 01864 502808
• e-mail: info@mountviewcaravanpark.co.uk
• website: www.mountviewcaravanpark.co.uk

Self-Catering
Carmichael Country Cottages,
Carmichael Estate Office, Westmains,
Carmichael, BIGGAR, Lanarkshire ML12 6PG
Tel: 01899 308336
• e-mail: chiefcarm@aol.com
• website: www.carmichael.co.uk/cottages

•PERTH & KINROSS

Hotel
Fortingall Hotel, Fortingall, ABERFELDY,
Perthshire PH15 2NQ Tel: 01887 830367
• e-mail: hotel@fortingallhotel.com
• website: www.fortingallhotel.com

Self-Catering
Loch Tay Lodges, Remony, Acharn,
ABERFELDY, Perthshire PH15 2HS
Tel: 01887 830209
• e-mail: remony@btinternet.com
• website: www.lochtaylodges.co.uk

Hotel
Lands of Loyal Hotel, ALYTH, Perthshire
PH11 8JQ Tel: 01828 633151
• e-mail: info@landsofloyal.com
• website: www.landsofloyal.com

Self-Catering
Laighwood Holidays, Laighwood,
Butterstone, BY DUNKELD,
Perthshire PH8 0HB Tel: 01350 724241
• e-mail: holidays@laighwood.co.uk
• website: www.laighwood.co.uk

•STIRLING & TROSSACHS

Guest House
Croftburn Bed & Breakfast, Croftamie,
DRYMEN, Loch Lomond G63 0HA
Tel: 01360 660796
• e-mail: johnreid@croftburn.fsnet.co.uk
• website: www.croftburn.co.uk

•SCOTTISH ISLANDS

•SKYE

Hotel & Restaurant
Royal Hotel, Bank Street, PORTREE, Isle of
Skye IV51 9BU Tel: 01478 612525
• e-mail: info@royal-hotel-skye.com
• website: www.royal-hotel-skye.com

•WALES

Self-Catering
Quality Cottages, Cerbid, Solva,
HAVERFORDWEST, Pembrokeshire
SA62 6YE Tel: 01348 837871
• website: www.qualitycottages.co.uk

•ANGLESEY & GWYNEDD

Caravan & Camping
Mr John Billingham, Islawrffordd Caravan
Park, Tal-y-Bont, Near BARMOUTH,
Gwynedd LL43 2BQ Tel: 01341 247269
• e-mail: info@islawrffordd.co.uk
• website: www.islawrffordd.co.uk

Country House
Sygun Fawr Country House, BEDDGELERT,
Gwynedd LL55 4NE Tel: 01766 890258
• e-mail: sygunfawr@aol.com
• website: www.sygunfawr.co.uk

Self-Catering / Caravans
Plas-y-Bryn Chalet Park, Bontnewydd,
CAERNARFON, Gwynedd LL54 7YE
Tel: 01286 672811
• www.plasybrynholidayscaernarfon.co.uk

Self-Catering within a Castle
BrynBras Castle, Llanrug,
Near CAERNARFON, Gwynedd LL55 4RE
Tel: 01286 870210
• e-mail: holidays@brynbrascastle.co.uk
• website: www.brynbrascastle.co.uk

Golf Club
Porthmadog Golf Club, Morfa Bychan,
PORTHMADOG, Gwynedd LL49 9UU
Tel: 01766 514124
• e-mail: secretary@porthmadog-golf-club.co.uk
• website: www.porthmadog-golf-club.co.uk

Golf Club
Anglesey Golf Club Ltd, Station Road,
RHOSNEIGR, Anglesey LL64 5QX
Tel: 01407 811202
• e-mail: info@theangleseygolfclub.com
• website: www.angleseygolfclub.co.uk

•NORTH WALES

Hotel
Fairy Glen Hotel, Beaver Bridge,
BETWS-Y-COED, Conwy, North Wales
LL24 0SH Tel: 01690 710269
• e-mail: fairyglen@youe.fsworld.co.uk
• website: www.fairyglenhotel.co.uk

Hotel
Sychnant Pass House, Sychnant Pass Road
CONWY LL32 8BJ Tel: 01492 596868
• e-mail: bre@sychnant-pass-house.co.uk
• website: www.sychnant-pass-house.co.uk

Golf Club
Denbigh Golf Club, Henllan Road, DENBIGH,
North Wales LL16 5AA Tel: 01745 816669
• e-mail: denbighgolfclub@aol.com
• website: www.denbighgolfclub.co.uk

Self-Catering Cottages
Glyn Uchaf, Conwy Old Road,
PENMAENMAWR, North Wales
LL34 6YS Tel: 01492 623737
• e-mail: john@baxter6055.freeserve.co.uk
• website: www.glyn-uchaf.co.uk

Golf Club
Rhuddlan Golf Club, Meliden Road,
RHUDDLAN, Denbighshire LL18 6LB
Tel: 01745 590217
• e-mail: secretary@rhuddlangolfclub.co.uk
• website: www.rhuddlangolfclub.co.uk

•CARMARTHENSHIRE

Faerm / B & B
Margaret Thomas, Plas Farm, Llangynog,
CARMARTHEN, Carmarthenshire SA33 5DB
Tel: 01267 211492
• website: www.plasfarm.co.uk

•CEREDIGION

Hotel
Queensbridge Hotel, Victoria Terrace,
ABERYSTWYTH, Ceredigion SY23 2DH
Tel: 01970 612343
• e-mail: queensbridgehotel@btinternet.com
• website: www.queensbridgehotel.com
www.queensbridgehotelaberystwyth.co.uk

• PEMBROKESHIRE

Hotel / Guest House
Ivybridge, Drim Mill, Dyffryn, Goodwick,
FISHGUARD, Pembrokeshire SA64 0JT
Tel: 01348 875366
• e-mail: ivybridge5366@aol.com
• website: www.ivybridgeleisure.co.uk

Country House
Angelica Rees, Heathfield House, Letterston,
NEAR FISHGUARD, Pembrokeshire
SA62 5EG Tel: 01348 840263
• e-mail: angelica.rees@virgin.net
• website: www.heathfieldaccommodation.co.uk

Hotel
Trewern Arms Hotel, Nevern, NEWPORT,
Pembrokeshire SA42 0NB
Tel: 01239 820395
• e-mail:
info@trewern-arms-pembrokeshire.co.uk
• www.trewern-arms-pembrokeshire.co.uk

Self-catering
Ffynnon Ddofn, ST DAVIDS, Pembrokeshire.
Contact: Mrs B. Rees White, Brick House
Farm, Burnham Road, Woodham Mortimer,
Maldon, Essex CM9 6SR
Tel: 01245 224611
• e-mail: daisypops@madasafish.com
• website: www.ffynnonddofn.co.uk

Farm Guest House
Mrs Morfydd Jones,
Lochmeyler Farm Guest House, Llandeloy,
Pen-y-Cwm, Near Solva, ST DAVIDS,
Pembrokeshire SA62 6LL
Tel: 01348 837724
• e-mail: stay@lochmeyler.co.uk
• website: www.lochmeyler.co.uk

Golf Club
Tenby Golf Club, The Burrows, TENBY,
Pembrokeshire SA70 7NP
Tel: 01834 842978
• e-mail: tenbygolfclub@uku.co.uk
• website: www.tenbygolf.co.uk

Self-catering
Mrs A Colledge, Gwarmacwydd, Llanfallteg, WHITLAND, Pembrokeshire SA34 0XH
Tel: 01437 563260
• website: www.davidsfarm.com

•POWYS

Farm
Caebetran Farm, Felinfach, BRECON, Powys LD3 0UL Tel: 01874 754460
• e-mail: hazelcaebetran@aol.com
• website:
caebetranfarmhousebedandbreakfastwales.com

Self-Catering
Tyn-Y-Castell, ELAN VALLEY, Powys
Contact: Joan Morgan, Old Bedw Farmhouse, Near Erwood, Builth Wells, Powys LD2 3LQ Tel: 01982 560402
• e-mail: oldbedw@lineone.net
• website: www.rhayader.co.uk/tynycastell

Self-Catering
Mrs Jones, Penllwyn Lodges, GARTHMYL, Powys SY15 6SB
Tel: 01686 640269
• e-mail: daphne.jones@onetel.net
• website: www.penllwynlodges.co.uk

Self-Catering
Old Stables Cottage & Old Dairy, Lane Farm, Paincastle, Builth Wells, HAY-ON-WYE, Powys LD2 3JS Tel: 01497 851 605
• e-mail: lanefarm@onetel.com
• website: www.lane-farm.co.uk

Self-Catering
Ann Reed, Madog's Wells, Llanfair Caereinion, WELSHPOOL, Powys SY21 0DE
Tel: 01938 810446
• e-mail: info@madogswells.co.uk
• website: www.madogswells.co.uk

•SOUTH WALES

Narrowboat Hire
Castle Narrowboats, Church Road Wharf, Gilwern, Monmouthshire NP7 0EP
Tel: 01873 830001
• e-mail: info@castlenarrowboats.co.uk
• website: www.castlenarrowboats.co.uk

B & B
George Lawrence, Half Moon Inn, Llanthony, ABERGAVENNY, Monmouthshire NP7 7NN
Tel: 01873 890611
• e-mail: halfmoon@llanthony.wanadoo.co.uk
• website: www.halfmoon-llanthony.co.uk

B & B / Self-Catering Cottages
Mrs Norma James, Wyrloed Lodge, Manmoel, BLACKWOOD, Caerphilly, South Wales NP12 0RN Tel: 01495 371198
• e-mail: norma.james@btinternet.com
• website: www.btinternet.com/~norma.james/

Guest House
Rosemary & Derek Ringer, Church Farm Guest House, Mitchel Troy, MONMOUTH, South Wales NP25 4HZ Tel: 01600 712176
• e-mail:
info@churchfarmguesthouse.eclipse.co.uk
• website: www.churchfarmmitcheltroy.co.uk

•IRELAND

CO. CLARE

Self-Catering
Ballyvaughan Village & Country Holiday Homes, BALLYVAUGHAN.
Contact: George Quinn, Frances Street, Kilrush, Co. Clare Tel: 00 353 65 9051977
• e-mail: vchh@iol.ie
• website: www.ballyvaughan-cottages.com

• CHANNEL ISLANDS

GUERNSEY

Self-Catering Apartments
Swallow Apartments, La Cloture, L'Ancresse, GUERNSEY Tel: 01481 249633
• e-mail: swallowapt@aol.com
• website: www.swallowapartments.com

Looking for Holiday Accommodation?

for details of hundreds of properties
throughout the UK, visit our website
www.holidayguides.com

FHG · K·U·P·E·R·A·R·D · **READERS' OFFER 2008**

LEIGHTON BUZZARD RAILWAY
Page's Park Station, Billington Road,
Leighton Buzzard, Bedfordshire LU7 4TN
Tel: 01525 373888
e-mail: info@buzzrail.co.uk
www.buzzrail.co.uk

One FREE adult/child with full-fare adult ticket
Valid 11/3/2008 - 28/10/2008

NOT TO BE USED IN CONJUNCTION WITH ANY OTHER OFFER

FHG · K·U·P·E·R·A·R·D · **READERS' OFFER 2008**

THE LIVING RAINFOREST
Hampstead Norreys,
Berkshire RG18 0TN
Tel: 01635 202444 • Fax: 01635 202440
e-mail: enquiries@livingrainforest.org
www.livingrainforest.org

One FREE child with each full paying adult.
Valid during 2008.

NOT TO BE USED IN CONJUNCTION WITH ANY OTHER OFFER

FHG · K·U·P·E·R·A·R·D · **READERS' OFFER 2008**

BEKONSCOT MODEL VILLAGE & RAILWAY
Warwick Road, Beaconsfield,
Buckinghamshire HP9 2PL
Tel: 01494 672919
e-mail: info@bekonscot.co.uk
www.bekonscot.com

One child FREE when accompanied by full-paying adult
Valid February to October 2008

NOT TO BE USED IN CONJUNCTION WITH ANY OTHER OFFER

FHG · K·U·P·E·R·A·R·D · **READERS' OFFER 2008**

BUCKINGHAMSHIRE RAILWAY CENTRE
Quainton Road Station, Quainton,
Aylesbury HP22 4BY
Tel & Fax: 01296 655720
e-mail: bucksrailcentre@btopenworld.com
www.bucksrailcentre.org

One child FREE with each full-paying adult
Not valid for Special Events

NOT TO BE USED IN CONJUNCTION WITH ANY OTHER OFFER

A 70-minute journey into the lost world of the English narrow gauge light railway. Features historic steam locomotives from many countries.

PETS MUST BE KEPT UNDER CONTROL AND NOT ALLOWED ON TRACKS

Open: Sundays and Bank Holiday weekends 11 March to 28 October. Additional days in summer.

Directions: on A4146 towards Hemel Hempstead, close to roundabout junction with A505.

Discover the exotic collection of tropical plants and animals inhabiting this living re-creation of the rainforest under glass. Explore your impact on the world's ecosystems using interactive displays. All-weather attraction. Children's play area.

Open: daily 10am to 5.15pm. Closed over Christmas period.

Directions: clearly signposted from J13 of M4. From Oxford take A34, exit at East Ilsley and follow signs. Nearest mainline station Newbury (8 miles). £1 'green discount' for visitors arriving by bus or bike.

Be a giant in a magical miniature world of make-believe depicting rural England in the 1930s. "A little piece of history that is forever England."

Open: 10am-5pm daily mid February to end October.

Directions: Junction 16 M25, Junction 2 M40.

A working steam railway centre. Steam train rides, miniature railway rides, large collection of historic preserved steam locomotives, carriages and wagons.

Open: Sundays and Bank Holidays April to October, plus Wednesdays in school holidays 10.30am to 4.30pm.

Directions: off A41 Aylesbury to Bicester Road, 6 miles north west of Aylesbury.

FHG
K·U·P·E·R·A·R·D

READERS' OFFER 2008

THE RAPTOR FOUNDATION
The Heath, St Ives Road,
Woodhurst, Huntingdon, Cambs PE28 3BT
Tel: 01487 741140 • Fax: 01487 841140
e-mail: heleowl@aol.com
www.raptorfoundation.org.uk

TWO for the price of ONE
Valid until end 2008 (not Bank Holidays)

FHG
K·U·P·E·R·A·R·D

READERS' OFFER 2008

SACREWELL FARM & COUNTRY CENTRE
Sacrewell, Thornhaugh,
Peterborough PE8 6HJ
Tel: 01780 782254
e-mail: info@sacrewell.fsnet.co.uk
www.sacrewell.org.uk

One child FREE with one full paying adult
Valid from March 1st to October 1st 2008

FHG
K·U·P·E·R·A·R·D

READERS' OFFER 2008

THE NATIONAL WATERWAYS MUSEUM
South Pier Road, Ellesmere Port,
Cheshire CH65 4FW
Tel: 0151-355 5017 • Fax: 0151-355 4079
ellesmereport@thewaterwaystrust.org.uk
www.nwm.org.uk/ellesmere

20% discount on standard admissions.
Valid during 2008.

FHG
K·U·P·E·R·A·R·D

READERS' OFFER 2008

CHINA CLAY COUNTRY PARK
Wheal Martyn, Carthew, St Austell,
Cornwall PL26 8XG
Tel & Fax: 01726 850362
e-mail: info@chinaclaycountry.co.uk
www.chinaclaycountry.co.uk

TWO for ONE adult entry, saving £7.50.
One voucher per person. Valid until July 2008.

Birds of Prey Centre offering audience participation in flying displays which are held 3 times daily. Tours, picnic area, gift shop, tearoom, craft shop.	**Open:** 10am-5pm all year except Christmas and New Year. **Directions:** follow brown tourist signs from B1040.

FHG GUIDES, ABBEY MILL BUSINESS CENTRE, PAISLEY PA1 1TJ • www.holidayguides.com

Farm animals, Shire Horse Centre, 18th century watermill and farmhouse, farm artifacts, caravan and camping, children's play areas. Cafe and farm & gift shop.	**Open:** all year. 9.30am to 5pm 1st March -30th Sept 10am-4pm 1st Oct to 28th Feb **Directions:** signposted off both A47 and A1.

FHG GUIDES, ABBEY MILL BUSINESS CENTRE, PAISLEY PA1 1TJ • www.holidayguides.com

Can you imagine your family living in a space measuring 6′ x 8′? Clamber aboard our collection of narrowboats. New interactive galleries, shop, cafe. Large free car park. Daily boat trips.	**Open:** 10am to 5pm daily **Directions:** Junction 9 off the M53, signposted.

FHG GUIDES, ABBEY MILL BUSINESS CENTRE, PAISLEY PA1 1TJ • www.holidayguides.com

The Country Park covers 26 acres and includes woodland and historic trails, picnic sites, children's adventure trail and award-winning cycle trail. Remains of a Victorian clay works complete with the largest working water wheel in Cornwall. Shop, cafe, exhibitions, museum.	**Open:** 10am-6pm daily (closed Christmas Day) **Directions:** two miles north of St Austell on the B3274. Follow brown tourist signs. 5 minutes from Eden Project.

FHG GUIDES, ABBEY MILL BUSINESS CENTRE, PAISLEY PA1 1TJ • www.holidayguides.com

FHG K·U·P·E·R·A·R·D

READERS' OFFER 2008

GEEVOR TIN MINE
Pendeen, Penzance,
Cornwall TR19 7EW
Tel: 01736 788662 • Fax: 01736 786059
e-mail: bookings@geevor.com
www.geevor.com

TWO for the price of ONE or £3.75 off a family ticket
Valid 02/01/2008 to 20/12/2008

NOT TO BE USED IN CONJUNCTION WITH ANY OTHER OFFER

FHG K·U·P·E·R·A·R·D

READERS' OFFER 2008

NATIONAL SEAL SANCTUARY
Gweek, Helston,
Cornwall TR12 6UG
Tel: 01326 221361
e-mail: seals@sealsanctuary.co.uk
www.sealsanctuary.co.uk

TWO for ONE - on purchase of another ticket of
equal or greater value. Valid until December 2008.

NOT TO BE USED IN CONJUNCTION WITH ANY OTHER OFFER

FHG K·U·P·E·R·A·R·D

READERS' OFFER 2008

TAMAR VALLEY DONKEY PARK
St Ann's Chapel, Gunnislake,
Cornwall PL18 9HW
Tel: 01822 834072
e-mail: info@donkeypark.com
www.donkeypark.com

50p OFF per person, up to 6 persons
Valid from Easter until end October 2008

NOT TO BE USED IN CONJUNCTION WITH ANY OTHER OFFER

FHG K·U·P·E·R·A·R·D

READERS' OFFER 2008

DUCKY'S PARK FARM
Moor Lane, Flookburgh, Grange-over-Sands
Cumbria LA11 7LS
Tel: 015395 59293 • Fax: 015395 58005
e-mail: donna@duckysparkfarm.co.uk
www.duckysparkfarm.co.uk

10% OFF admission price
Valid during 2008

NOT TO BE USED IN CONJUNCTION WITH ANY OTHER OFFER

Geevor is the largest mining history site in the UK in a spectacular setting on Cornwall's Atlantic coast. Guided underground tour, many surface buildings, museum, cafe, gift shop. Free parking.

Open: daily except Saturdays 10am to 4pm

Directions: 7 miles from Penzance beside the B3306 Land's End to St Ives coast road

Britain's leading grey seal rescue centre

Open: daily (except Christmas Day) from 10am

Directions: from A30 follow signs to Helston, then brown tourist signs to Seal Sanctuary.

Cornwall's only Donkey Sanctuary set in 14 acres overlooking the beautiful Tamar Valley. Donkey rides, rabbit warren, goat hill, children's playgrounds, cafe and picnic area. New all-weather play barn.

Open: Easter to end Oct: daily 10am to 5.30pm. Nov to March: weekends and all school holidays 10.30am to 4.30pm

Directions: just off A390 between Callington and Gunnislake at St Ann's Chapel.

Children's open farm animal interaction centre. Large indoor soft play, bouncy castle, go-karts, driving school, playground, cafe. Full disabled facilities, wheelchair-friendly.

Open: March to October 10.30am to 4pm

Directions: M6 J36. Follow A590 through Grange-over-Sands on the B5277. From Barrow-in-Furness turn right at Haverthwaite on to the B278 and follow signs to Flookburgh.

FHG
·K·U·P·E·R·A·R·D·
**READERS'
OFFER
2008**

CARS OF THE STARS MOTOR MUSEUM
Standish Street, Keswick,
Cumbria CA12 5HH
Tel: 017687 73757
e-mail: cotsmm@aol.com
www.carsofthestars.com

*One child free with two paying adults
Valid during 2008*

NOT TO BE USED IN CONJUNCTION WITH ANY OTHER OFFER

FHG
·K·U·P·E·R·A·R·D·
**READERS'
OFFER
2008**

ESKDALE HISTORIC WATER MILL
Mill Cottage, Boot, Eskdale,
Cumbria CA19 1TG
Tel: 019467 23335
e-mail: david.king403@tesco.net
www.eskdale.info

Eskdale
Historic
Water Mill

*Two children FREE with two adults
Valid during 2008*

NOT TO BE USED IN CONJUNCTION WITH ANY OTHER OFFER

FHG
·K·U·P·E·R·A·R·D·
**READERS'
OFFER
2008**

CRICH TRAMWAY VILLAGE
Crich, Matlock
Derbyshire DE4 5DP
Tel: 01773 854321 • Fax: 01773 854320
e-mail: enquiry@tramway.co.uk
www.tramway.co.uk

CRICH
TRAMWAY
VILLAGE

*One child FREE with every full-paying adult
Valid during 2008*

NOT TO BE USED IN CONJUNCTION WITH ANY OTHER OFFER

FHG
·K·U·P·E·R·A·R·D·
**READERS'
OFFER
2008**

DEVONSHIRE COLLECTION OF PERIOD COSTUME
Totnes Costume Museum,
Bogan House, 43 High Street,
Totnes,
Devon TQ9 5NP

*FREE child with a paying adult with voucher
Valid from Spring Bank Holiday to end of Sept 2008*

NOT TO BE USED IN CONJUNCTION WITH ANY OTHER OFFER

A collection of cars from film and TV,
including Chitty Chitty Bang Bang,
James Bond's Aston Martin,
Del Boy's van, Fab1 and many more.

PETS MUST BE KEPT ON LEAD

Open: daily 10am-5pm.
Open February half term,
lst April to end November,
also weekends in December.

Directions: in centre of Keswick
close to car park.

The oldest working mill in England
with 18th century oatmeal
machinery running daily.

DOGS ON LEADS

Open: 11am to 5pm April to Sept.
(may be closed Saturdays & Mondays)

Directions: near inland terminus of
Ravenglass & Eskdale Railway or over
Hardknott Pass.

A superb family day out in the
atmosphere of a bygone era.
Explore the recreated period street
and fascinating exhibitions.
Unlimited tram rides are free with
entry. Play areas, woodland walk and
sculpture trail, shops, tea rooms,
pub, restaurant and lots more.

Open: daily April to October 10 am
to 5.30pm, weekends in winter.

Directions: eight miles from M1
Junction 28, follow brown and white
signs for "Tramway Museum".

Themed exhibition, changed
annually, based in a Tudor house.
Collection contains items of dress for
women, men and children from 17th
century to 1980s, from high fashion
to everyday wear.

Open: Open from Spring Bank
Holiday to end September. 11am to
5pm Tuesday to Friday.

Directions: centre of town, opposite
Market Square. Mini bus up High
Street stops outside.

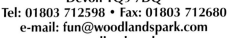

*All weather fun - guaranteed!
Unique combination of indoor/outdoor
attractions. 3 Watercoasters, Toboggan
Run, Arctic Gliders, boats, 15 Playzones
for all ages. Biggest indoor venture zone
in UK with 5 floors of play and rides.
New Big Fun Farm with U-drive Tractor
ride, Pedal Town and Yard Racers.
Falconry Centre.*

Open: mid-March to November
open daily at 9.30am. Winter: open
weekends and local school holidays.

Directions: 5 miles from Dartmouth
on A3122. Follow brown tourist signs
from A38.

*This award-winning Victorian mining
museum makes a great day out for
all the family. Hands-on activities
plus unforgettable mine tour.
Green Tourism Gold Award 2007.*

Open: Easter weekend +April 1st to
October 31st 10.30am to 5pm daily.

Directions: alongside A689, midway
between Stanhope and Alston in the
heart of the North Pennines.

*Children's farm and petting centre
with lots of farm animals and exotic
animals too, including camels, otters,
monkeys, meerkats and lots more.
Lots of hands-on, with bottle
feeding, reptile handling and bunny
cuddling happening daily.*

Open: March to Oct: 10am-5pm
daily; Nov to Feb 10am to 4pm daily.
Closed Christmas, Boxing Day and
New Year's Day.

Directions: A181 from A19, head
towards coast; signposted from there.

*A real working organic dairy farm in
the Severn Vale. St Augustine's is a
typical dairy farm of over 100 acres
where the everyday farm life will go
on around you.*

Open: March to October open daily
11am to 5pm (except term-time
Mondays).

Directions: leave M5 by J13 to A38.
Half a mile south turn right on B4071
and follow brown tourist signs.

FHG

·K·U·P·E·R·A·R·D·

READERS' OFFER 2008

AVON VALLEY RAILWAY
Bitton Station, Bath Road, Bitton,
Bristol BS30 6HD
Tel: 0117 932 5538
e-mail: info@avonvalleyrailway.org
www.avonvalleyrailway.org

One FREE child with every fare-paying adult
Valid May - Oct 2008 (not 'Day Out with Thomas' events)

FHG

·K·U·P·E·R·A·R·D·

READERS' OFFER 2008

EXPLOSION! MUSEUM OF NAVAL FIREPOWER
Priddy's Hard, Gosport
Hampshire PO12 4LE
Tel: 023 9250 5600 • Fax: 023 9250 5605
e-mail: info@explosion.org.uk
www.explosion.org.uk

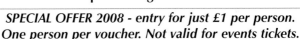

SPECIAL OFFER 2008 - entry for just £1 per person.
One person per voucher. Not valid for events tickets.

FHG

·K·U·P·E·R·A·R·D·

READERS' OFFER 2008

QUEX MUSEUM, HOUSE & GARDENS
Quex Park, Birchington
Kent CT7 0BH
Tel: 01843 842168 • Fax: 01843 846661
e-mail: enquiries@quexmuseum.org
www.quexmuseum.org

QUEX
MUSEUM.HOUSE
GARDENS
The Powell-Cotton Collection

One adult FREE with each full-paying adult on
presentation of voucher. Valid until 31 December 2008

FHG

·K·U·P·E·R·A·R·D·

READERS' OFFER 2008

CHISLEHURST CAVES
Old Hill, Chislehurst,
Kent BR7 5NB
Tel: 020 8467 3264 • Fax: 020 8295 0407
e-mail: info@chislehurstcaves.co.uk
www.chislehurstcaves.co.uk

CHISLEHURST CAVES

FREE child entry with full paying adult.
Valid until end 2008 (not Bank Holiday weekends)

The Avon Valley Railway offers a whole new experience for some, and a nostalgic memory for others.

PETS MUST BE KEPT ON LEADS AND OFF TRAIN SEATS

Open: Steam trains operate every Sunday, Easter to October, plus Bank Holidays and Christmas.

Directions: on the A431 midway between Bristol and Bath at Bitton.

FHG GUIDES, ABBEY MILL BUSINESS CENTRE, PAISLEY PA1 1TJ • www.holidayguides.com

---

A hands-on interactive museum, telling the story of naval warfare from gunpowder to modern missiles. Also fascinating social history of how 2500 women worked on the site during World War II. Gift shop and Waterside Coffee Shop with stunning harbour views.

Open: Saturday and Sunday 10am to 4pm (last entry one hour before closing).

Directions: M27 to J11, follow A32 to Gosport; signposted. By rail to Portsmouth Harbour, then ferry to Gosport.

FHG GUIDES, ABBEY MILL BUSINESS CENTRE, PAISLEY PA1 1TJ • www.holidayguides.com

---

World-ranking Museum incorporating Kent's finest Regency house. Gardens with peacocks, woodland walk, walled garden, maze and fountains. Children's activities and full events programme. Tearoom and gift shop.

Open: mid-March-Nov: Sun-Thurs 11am-5pm (House opens 2pm). Winter: Sundays 1-3.30pm (Museum and Gardens only).

Directions: A2 to Margate, on entering Birchington turn right at church into Park Lane; Quex Museum signposted.

FHG GUIDES, ABBEY MILL BUSINESS CENTRE, PAISLEY PA1 1TJ • www.holidayguides.com

---

Miles of mystery and history beneath your feet! Grab a lantern and get ready for an amazing underground adventure. Your whole family can travel back in time as you explore this labyrinth of dark mysterious passageways. See the caves, church, Druid altar and more.

Open: Wed to Sun from 10am; last tour 4pm. Open daily during local school and Bank holidays (except Christmas). Entrance by guided tour only.

Directions: A222 between A20 and A21; at Chislehurst Station turn into Station Approach; turn right at end, then right again into Caveside Close.

FHG GUIDES, ABBEY MILL BUSINESS CENTRE, PAISLEY PA1 1TJ • www.holidayguides.com

WINGHAM WILDLIFE PARK
Rusham Road, Wingham,
Canterbury, Kent CT3 1JL
Tel: 01227 720836
gabr@winghamwildlifepark.co.uk
www.winghamwildlifepark.co.uk

One FREE child entry with two full paying adults

NOT TO BE USED IN CONJUNCTION WITH ANY OTHER OFFER

THE HOP FARM AT THE KENTISH OAST VILLAGE
Beltring, Paddock Wood,
Kent TN12 6PY
Tel: 01622 872068 • Fax: 01622 870800
e-mail: info@thehopfarm.co.uk
www.thehopfarm.co.uk

Admit one child HALF PRICE with a full paying adult.
Valid until March 2008.

NOT TO BE USED IN CONJUNCTION WITH ANY OTHER OFFER

MUSEUM OF KENT LIFE
Lock Lane, Sandling, Maidstone,
Kent ME14 3AU
Tel: 01622 763936 • Fax: 01622 662024
e-mail: enquiries@museum-kentlife.co.uk
www.museum-kentlife.co.uk

MUSEUM OF
KENT LIFE

One child FREE with one full-paying adult
Valid during 2008

NOT TO BE USED IN CONJUNCTION WITH ANY OTHER OFFER

DOCKER PARK FARM
Arkholme, Carnforth,
Lancashire LA6 1AR
Tel & Fax: 015242 21331
e-mail: info@dockerparkfarm.co.uk
www.dockerparkfarm.co.uk

One FREE child per one paying adult (one voucher per child)
Valid from January to December 2008

NOT TO BE USED IN CONJUNCTION WITH ANY OTHER OFFER

206

Come and join us .. .take a walk on the wildside ... see meerkats, lemurs, reptile house, birds of prey, pet village, parrot house and much more. With an adventure playground and full facilities, you'll be sure to enjoy your day.

Open: daily 10am to 6pm or dusk (whichever is earlier). Guide dogs only.

Directions: on the A257 main Sandwich to Canterbury road, just outside the village.

FHG GUIDES, ABBEY MILL BUSINESS CENTRE, PAISLEY PA1 1TJ • www.holidayguides.com

Set in 400 acres of unspoilt Kent countryside, this once working hop farm is one of Kent's most popular attractions. The spectacular oast village is home to an indoor and outdoor play area, interactive museum, shire horses and an animal farm, as well as hosting special events throughout the year.

Open: 10am-5pm daily (last admission 4pm).

Directions: A228 Paddock Wood

FHG GUIDES, ABBEY MILL BUSINESS CENTRE, PAISLEY PA1 1TJ • www.holidayguides.com

Kent's award-winning open air museum is home to a collection of historic buildings which house interactive exhibitions on life over the last 150 years.

Open: seven days a week from February to start November, 10am to 5pm.

Directions: Junction 6 off M20, follow signs to Aylesford.

FHG GUIDES, ABBEY MILL BUSINESS CENTRE, PAISLEY PA1 1TJ • www.holidayguides.com

We are a working farm, with lots of animals to see and touch. Enjoy a walk round the Nature Trail or refreshments in the tearoom. Lots of activities during school holidays.

Open: Summer: daily 10.30am- 5pm. Winter: weekends only 10.30am-4pm.

Directions: Junction 35 off M6, take B6254 towards Kirkby Lonsdale, then follow the brown signs.

FHG GUIDES, ABBEY MILL BUSINESS CENTRE, PAISLEY PA1 1TJ • www.holidayguides.com

FHG
K·U·P·E·R·A·R·D
READERS'
OFFER
2008

SKEGNESS NATURELAND SEAL SANCTUARY
North Parade, Skegness,
Lincolnshire PE25 1DB
Tel: 01754 764345
e-mail: natureland@fsbdial.co.uk
www.skegnessnatureland.co.uk

Natureland Seal Sanctuary

Free entry for one child when accompanied by full-paying adult. Valid during 2008.

FHG
K·U·P·E·R·A·R·D
READERS'
OFFER
2008

THE BEATLES STORY
Britannia Vaults, Albert Dock
Liverpool L3 4AD
Tel: 0151-709 1963 • Fax: 0151-708 0039
e-mail: info@beatlesstory.com
www.beatlesstory.com

One FREE child with one full paying adult
Valid during 2008

FHG

K·U·P·E·R·A·R·D
READERS'
OFFER
2008

BRESSINGHAM STEAM & GARDENS
Low Road, Bressingham, Diss,
Norfolk IP22 2AB
Tel: 01379 686900 • Fax: 01379 686907
e-mail: info@bressingham.co.uk
www.bressingham.co.uk

One child FREE with two paying adults
Valid Easter to October 2008

FHG

K·U·P·E·R·A·R·D
READERS'
OFFER
2008

FERRY FARM PARK
Ferry Farm, Boat Lane, Hoveringham
Nottinghamshire NG14 7JP
Tel & Fax: 0115 966 4512
e-mail: enquiries@ferryfarm.co.uk
www.ferryfarm.co.uk

20% OFF admission price.
Valid during 2008.

Well known for rescuing and rehabilitating orphaned and injured seal pups found washed ashore on Lincolnshire beaches. Also: penguins, aquarium, pets' corner, reptiles, Floral Palace (tropical birds and butterflies etc).

Open: daily from 10am. Closed Christmas/Boxing/New Year's Days.

Directions: at the north end of Skegness seafront.

A unique visitor attraction that transports you on an enlightening and atmospheric journey into the life, times, culture and music of the Beatles. See how four young lads from Liverpool were propelled into the dizzy heights of worldwide fame and fortune to become the greatest band of all time. Hear the story unfold through the 'Living History' audio guide narrated by John Lennon's sister, Julia.

Open: daily 10am to 6pm (last admisssion 5pm) all year round (excl. 25/26 December)

Directions: located within Liverpool's historic Albert Dock.

Explore one of Europe's leading steam collections, take a ride over 5 miles of narrow gauge steam railway, wander through beautiful gardens, or visit the only official 'Dads' Army' exhibition. Two restaurants and garden centre.

Open: Easter to October 10.30am - 5pm

Directions: 2½ miles west of Diss and 14 miles east of Thetford on the A1066; follow brown tourist signs.

Family-run farm park set in beautiful countryside next to river. 20-acre site with animal handling, large indoor soft play area, go-karts, trampolines, pedal tractors, swings, slides, zipline and assault course.

Open: daily 10am to 5.30pm April to end September. Closed Mondays except Bank Holidays and during school holidays. Please check for winter opening hours.

Directions: off A612 Nottingham to Southwell road.

A collection of 70 aircraft and cockpit sections from across the history of aviation. Extensive aero engine and artefact displays.

Open: daily from 10am (closed Christmas period and New Year's Day).

Directions: follow brown and white signs from A1, A46, A17 and A1133.

Travel back in time with Robin Hood and his merry men on an adventure-packed theme tour, exploring the intriguing and mysterious story of their legendary tales of Medieval England. Enjoy film shows, live performances, adventure rides and even try archery! Are you brave enough to join Robin on his quest for good against evil?

Open: 10am-5.30pm, last admission 4.30pm.

Directions: follow the brown and white tourist information signs whilst heading towards the city centre.

See the steam trains from the golden age of the Great Western Railway. Steam locomotives in the original engine shed, a reconstructed country branch line, and a re-creation of Brunel's original broad gauge railway. On Steam Days there are rides in the 1930s carriages.

Open: Sat/Sun all year; daily 21 June to 31 August + school holidays. 10am-5pm weekends and Steam Days, 10am-4pm other days and in winter.

Directions: at Didcot Parkway rail station; on A4130, signposted from M4 (Junction 13) and A34

A real children's paradise. A complete hands-on experience, from feeding the lambs and sheep, goat racing, petting the lizards and talking to the parrots to candle dipping, mini quad biking, pony rides and other craft activities. Hoo Farm has everything for a family day out.

Open: follow brown tourist signs from M54 J6, A442 at Leegomery or A518 at Donnington

Directions: 10am-6pm (last entries 5pm) Tues-Sun during term times and every day during school holidays and Bank Holidays.

**READERS'
OFFER
2008**

EXMOOR FALCONRY & ANIMAL FARM
Allerford, Near Porlock, Minehead,
Somerset TA24 8HJ
Tel: 01643 862816
e-mail: exmoor.falcon@virgin.net
www.exmoorfalconry.co.uk

*10% off entry to Falconry Centre
Valid during 2008*

NOT TO BE USED IN CONJUNCTION WITH ANY OTHER OFFER

**READERS'
OFFER
2008**

FLEET AIR ARM MUSEUM
RNAS Yeovilton, Ilchester,
Somerset BA22 8HT
Tel: 01935 840565
e-mail: enquiries@fleetairarm.com
www.fleetairarm.com

Fleet Air
Arm Museum

*One child FREE with full paying adult
Valid during 2008 except Bank Holidays*

NOT TO BE USED IN CONJUNCTION WITH ANY OTHER OFFER

**READERS'
OFFER
2008**

THE HELICOPTER MUSEUM
The Heliport, Locking Moor Road,
Weston-Super-Mare BS24 8PP
Tel: 01934 635227• Fax: 01934 645230
e-mail: helimuseum@btconnect.com
www.helicoptermuseum.co.uk

*One child FREE with two full-paying adults
Valid from April to October 2008*

NOT TO BE USED IN CONJUNCTION WITH ANY OTHER OFFER

**READERS'
OFFER
2008**

YESTERDAY'S WORLD
High Street, Battle, E. Sussex TN33 0AQ
Tel: 01424 775378 (24hr info)
Enquiries/bookings: 01424 893938
e-mail: info@yesterdaysworld.co.uk
www.yesterdaysworld.co.uk

*One child FREE when accompanied by one
full-paying adult. Valid until end 2008*

NOT TO BE USED IN CONJUNCTION WITH ANY OTHER OFFER

212

Falconry centre with animals - flying displays, animal handling, feeding and bottle feeding - in 15th century NT farmyard setting on Exmoor. Also falconry and outdoor activities, hawk walks and riding.

Open: 10.30am to 5pm daily

Directions: A39 west of Minehead, turn right at Allerford, half a mile along lane on left.

Europe's largest naval aviation collection with over 40 aircraft on display , including Concorde 002 and Ark Royal Aircraft Carrier Experience. Situated on an operational naval air station.

Open: open daily April to October 10am-5.30pm; November to March 10am-4.30pm (closed Mon and Tues).

Directions: just off A303/A37 on B3151 at Ilchester. Yeovil rail station 10 miles.

The world's largest helicopter collection - over 70 exhibits, includes two royal helicopters, Russian Gunship and Vietnam veterans plus many award-winning exhibits. Cafe, shop. Flights.
PETS MUST BE KEPT UNDER CONTROL

Open: Wednesday to Sunday 10am to 5.30pm. Daily during school Easter and Summer holidays and Bank Holiday Mondays. November to March: 10am to 4.30pm

Directions: Junction 21 off M5 then follow the propellor signs.

The past is brought to life at one of the South East's best loved family attractions. 100,000+ nostalgic artefacts, set in a charming 15th century house and country garden. New attractions and tearooms.

Open: 9.30am to 6pm (last admission 4.45pm, one hour earlier in winter). Closing times may vary – phone or check website.

Directions: just off A21 in Battle High Street opposite the Abbey.

213

PARADISE PARK & GARDENS
Avis Road, Newhaven,
East Sussex BN9 0DH
Tel: 01273 512123 • Fax: 01273 616000
e-mail: enquiries@paradisepark.co.uk
www.paradisepark.co.uk

READERS' OFFER 2008

*Admit one FREE child with one adult
paying full entrance price. Valid during 2008*

NOT TO BE USED IN CONJUNCTION WITH ANY OTHER OFFER

WILDERNESS WOOD
Hadlow Down, Near Uckfield,
East Sussex TN22 4HJ
Tel: 01825 830509• Fax: 01825 830977
e-mail: enquiries@wildernesswood.co.uk
www.wildernesswood.co.uk

READERS' OFFER 2008

*one FREE admission with a full-paying adult
Valid during 2008 (not for Special Events/Bank Holidays)*

NOT TO BE USED IN CONJUNCTION WITH ANY OTHER OFFER

EARNLEY BUTTERFLIES & GARDENS
133 Almodington Lane, Earnley, Chichester,
West Sussex PO20 7JR
Tel: 01243 512637
e-mail: earnleygardens@msn.com
www.earnleybutterfliesandgardens.co.uk

READERS' OFFER 2008

*£2 per person offer normal entry prices.
Valid late March to end October 2008.*

NOT TO BE USED IN CONJUNCTION WITH ANY OTHER OFFER

STRATFORD BUTTERFLY FARM
Swan's Nest Lane, Stratford-upon-Avon
Warwickshire CV37 7LS
Tel: 01789 299288 • Fax: 01789 415878
e-mail: sales@butterflyfarm.co.uk
www.butterflyfarm.co.uk

READERS' OFFER 2008

*Admit TWO for the price of ONE
Valid until 31/12/2008*

NOT TO BE USED IN CONJUNCTION WITH ANY OTHER OFFER

Discover 'Planet Earth' for an unforgettable experience. A unique Museum of Life, Dinosaur Safari, beautiful Water Gardens with fish and wildfowl, plant houses, themed gardens, Heritage Trail, miniature railway. Playzone includes crazy golf and adventure play areas. Garden Centre and Terrace Cafe.

Open: open daily, except Christmas Day and Boxing Day.

Directions: signposted off A26 and A259.

FHG GUIDES, ABBEY MILL BUSINESS CENTRE, PAISLEY PA1 1TJ • www.holidayguides.com

---

Wilderness Wood is a unique family-run working woodland park in the Sussex High Weald. Explore trails and footpaths, enjoy local cakes and ices, try the adventure playground. Many special events and activities. Parties catered for. Green Tourism Gold Award.

Open: daily 10am to 5.30pm or dusk if earlier.

Directions: on the south side of the A272 in the village of Hadlow Down. Signposted with a brown tourist sign.

FHG GUIDES, ABBEY MILL BUSINESS CENTRE, PAISLEY PA1 1TJ • www.holidayguides.com

---

3 attractions in 1. Tropical butterflies, exotic animals of many types in our Noah's Ark Rescue Centre. Theme gardens with a free competition for kids. Rejectamenta - the nostalgia museum.

Open: 10am - 6pm daily late March to end October.

Directions: signposted from A27/A286 junction at Chichester.

FHG GUIDES, ABBEY MILL BUSINESS CENTRE, PAISLEY PA1 1TJ • www.holidayguides.com

---

Wander through a tropical rainforest with a myriad of multicoloured butterflies, sunbirds and koi carp. See fascinating animals in Insect City and view deadly spiders in perfect safety in Arachnoland.

Open: daily except Christmas Day. 10am-6pm summer, 10am-dusk winter.

Directions: on south bank of River Avon opposite Royal Shakespeare Theatre. Easily accessible from town centre, 5 minutes' walk.

FHG GUIDES, ABBEY MILL BUSINESS CENTRE, PAISLEY PA1 1TJ • www.holidayguides.com

215

FHG

·K·U·P·E·R·A·R·D·

READERS'
OFFER
2008

HATTON FARM VILLAGE AT HATTON COUNTRY WORLD
Dark Lane, Hatton, Near Warwick,
Warwickshire CV35 8XA
Tel: 01926 843411
e-mail: hatton@hattonworld.com
www.hattonworld.com

*Admit one child FREE with one full-paying adult day ticket. Valid during
2008 except Bank Holidays or for entrance to Santa's Grotto promotion.*

NOT TO BE USED IN CONJUNCTION WITH ANY OTHER OFFER

FHG

·K·U·P·E·R·A·R·D·

READERS'
OFFER
2008

AVONCROFT MUSEUM
Stoke Heath,
Bromsgrove,
Worcestershire B60 4JR
Tel: 01527 831363 • Fax: 01527 876934
www.avoncroft.org.uk

*One FREE child with one full-paying adult
Valid from March to November 2008*

NOT TO BE USED IN CONJUNCTION WITH ANY OTHER OFFER

FHG

·K·U·P·E·R·A·R·D·

READERS'
OFFER
2008

EMBSAY & BOLTON ABBEY STEAM RAILWAY
Bolton Abbey Station, Skipton,
North Yorkshire BD23 6AF
Tel: 01756 710614
e-mail: embsay.steam@btinternet.com
www.embsayboltonabbeyrailway.org.uk

EMBSAY &
BOLTON ABBEY
STEAM RAILWAY

*One adult travels FREE when accompanied by a full fare paying
adult (does not include Special Event days). Valid during 2008.*

NOT TO BE USED IN CONJUNCTION WITH ANY OTHER OFFER

FHG

·K·U·P·E·R·A·R·D·

READERS'
OFFER
2008

WORLD OF JAMES HERRIOT
23 Kirkgate, Thirsk,
North Yorkshire YO7 1PL
Tel: 01845 524234
Fax: 01845 525333
www.worldofjamesherriot.org

HERRIOT

*Admit TWO for the price of ONE (one voucher per
transaction only). Valid until October 2008*

NOT TO BE USED IN CONJUNCTION WITH ANY OTHER OFFER

Hatton Farm Village offers a wonderful mix of farmyard animals, adventure play, shows, demonstrations, and events, all set in the stunning Warwickshire countryside.

Open: daily 10am-5pm (4pm during winter). Closed Christmas Day and Boxing Day.

Directions: 5 minutes from M40 (J15), A46 towards Coventry, then just off A4177 (follow brown tourist signs).

A fascinating world of historic buildings covering 7 centuries, rescued and rebuilt on an open-air site in the heart of the Worcestershire countryside.

PETS ON LEADS ONLY

Open: July and August all week. March to November varying times, please telephone for details.

Directions: A38 south of Bromsgrove, near Junction 1 of M42, Junction 5 of M5.

Steam trains operate over a 4½ mile line from Bolton Abbey Station to Embsay Station. Many family events including Thomas the Tank Engine take place during major Bank Holidays.

Open: steam trains run every Sunday throughout the year and up to 7 days a week in summer. 10.30am to 4.30pm

Directions: Embsay Station signposted from the A59 Skipton by-pass; Bolton Abbey Station signposted from the A59 at Bolton Abbey.

Visit James Herriot's original house recreated as it was in the 1940s. Television sets used in the series 'All Creatures Great and Small'. There is a children's interactive gallery with life-size model farm animals and three rooms dedicated to the history of veterinary medicine.

Open: daily. Easter-Oct 10am-5pm; Nov-Easter 11am to 4pm

Directions: follow signs off A1 or A19 to Thirsk, then A168, off Thirsk market place

Visit the FHG website

www.holidayguides.com

for details of the wide choice of accommodation

featured in the full range of FHG titles

All types of birds of prey exhibited here, from owls and kestrels to eagles and vultures. Special flying displays 12 noon, 1.30pm and 3pm. Bird handling courses arranged for either half or full days.

GUIDE DOGS ONLY

Open: 10am to 4.30pm summer 10am to 4pm winter

Directions: on main A65 trunk road outside Settle. Follow brown direction signs.

FHG GUIDES, ABBEY MILL BUSINESS CENTRE, PAISLEY PA1 1TJ • www.holidayguides.com

---

Dinostar features an exhibition of dinosaurs and fossils. Highlights include a T-Rex skull, Triceratops bones you can touch, and our unique dinosaur sound box.

Open: 11am to 5pm Wednesday to Sunday.

Directions: in the Fruit Market area of Hull's Old Town, close to The Deep and Hull Marina.

FHG GUIDES, ABBEY MILL BUSINESS CENTRE, PAISLEY PA1 1TJ • www.holidayguides.com

---

A fascinating display of railway carriages and a wide range of railway items telling the story of rail travel over the years.

ALL PETS MUST BE KEPT ON LEADS

Open: daily 11am to 4.30pm

Directions: approximately one mile from Keighley on A629 Halifax road. Follow brown tourist signs

FHG GUIDES, ABBEY MILL BUSINESS CENTRE, PAISLEY PA1 1TJ • www.holidayguides.com

---

Please note

All the information in this book is given in good faith in the belief that it is correct. However, the publishers cannot guarantee the facts given in these pages, neither are they responsible for changes in policy, ownership or terms that may take place after the date of going to press.

Readers should always satisfy themselves that the facilities they require are available and that the terms, if quoted, still apply.

**Sacrewell Farm
& Country Centre**
*Thornaugh, Peterborough
Cambridgeshire*
See Readers' Offer Voucher

Cars of the Stars Museun
Keswick, Cumbria
ee Readers' Offer Voucher

Crich Tramway Village
*Crich, Matlock
Derbyshire*
e Readers' Offer Voucher

Woodlands
Blackawton, Dartmouth
Devon
See Readers' Offer Voucher

Hoo Farm Animal Kingdom
Preston-on-the-Weald-Moors
Telford, Shropshire
See Readers' Offer Voucher

Galloway Wildlife Conservation Park
Lochfergus, Kirkcudbright,
Dumfries & Galloway
See Readers' Offer Voucher

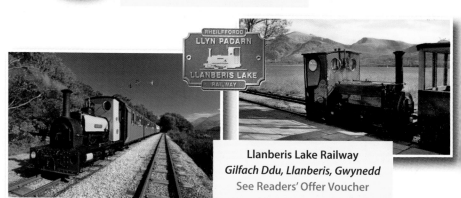

Llanberis Lake Railway
Gilfach Ddu, Llanberis, Gwynedd
See Readers' Offer Voucher

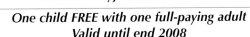

28-acre theme park with over 100 nursery rhyme characters, set in beautifully landscaped gardens. Shop and restaurant on site.

Open: 1st March to 31st October: daily 10am to 6pm; 1st Nov to end Feb: Sat/Sun only 11am to 4pm

Directions: 6 miles west of Aberdeen off B9077

Visitor Centre dedicated to the much-loved Scottish writer Lewis Grassic Gibbon. Exhibition, cafe, gift shop. Outdoor children's play area. Disabled access throughout.

Open: daily April to October 10am to 4.30pm. Groups by appointment including evenings.

Directions: on the B967, accessible and signposted from both A90 and A92.

19th century prison with fully restored 1820 courtroom and two prisons. Guides in uniform as warders, prisoners and matron. Remember your camera!

Open: April to October 9.30am-6pm (last admission 5pm); November to March 10am-5pm (last admission 4pm)

Directions: A83 to Campbeltown

Scotland's seafaring heritage is among the world's richest and you can relive the heyday of Scottish shipping at the Maritime Museum.

Open: 1st April to 31st October - 10am-5pm

Directions: situated on Irvine harbourside and only a 10 minute walk from Irvine train station.

The wild animal conservation centre of Southern Scotland. A varied collection of over 150 animals from all over the world can be seen within natural woodland settings. Picnic areas, cafe/gift shop, outdoor play area, woodland walks, close animal encounters.

Open: 10am to dusk 1st February to 30 November.

Directions: follow brown tourist signs from A75; one mile from Kirkcudbright on the B727.

Visitors can experience the thrill of a guided tour into an 18thC lead mine, explore the two period cottages, visit the second oldest subscription library and investigate the Visitor & Exhibition Centre. Taster sessions of gold panning available July and August.

Open: 1 April - 30 June: 11am-4.30pm July, August and Bank Holidays: 10am -5pm.

Directions: off M74. J14 if travelling north, J13 if travelling south.

A fantastic display of gems, crystals, minerals and fossils. An experience you'll treasure forever. Gift shop, tearoom and AV display.

Open: Summer - 9.30am to 5.30pm daily; Winter - 10am to 4pm daily. Closed Christmas to end January.

Directions: follow signs from A75 Dumfries/Stranraer.

Indoor adventure play area, farm park, toyshop and cafe. A great day out for all the family, with sledge and zip slides, mini-golf, trampolines, bumper boats, pottery painting and so much more.

Open: Monday to Saturday 10am-5.30pm.

Directions: just off the A75/A701 roundabout heading for Moffat and Edinburgh.

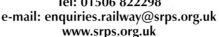

visitscotland 5-Star Attraction with two floors of interactive exhibitions, a 'Magic Helmet' tour of the pithead, re-created coal road and coal face, and new Big Stuff tour. Largest working winding engine in Britain.

Open: daily. Summer: 10am to 5pm (last tour 3.30pm). Winter: 10am to 4pm (last tour 2.30pm)

Directions: 5 minutes from Sherrifhall Roundabout on Edinburgh City Bypass on A7 south

See free-flying exotic butterflies in a tropical rainforest paradise, iguanas roaming free in jungle flora, and small birds darting in and out of the flowers. Have close encounters of the crawly kind in the 'Bugs & Beasties' exhibition that includes arrow frogs, tarantulas, amazing leaf-cutter ants and a unique Scottish Honey Bee display.

Open: daily. 9.30am-5.30pm summer, 10am-5pm winter.

Directions: located just off the Edinburgh City Bypass at the Gilmerton exit or Sherrifhall roundabout.

Steam and heritage diesel passenger trains from Bo'ness to Birkhill for guided tours of Birkhill fireclay mines. Explore the history of Scotland's railways in the Scottish Railway Exhibition. Coffee shop and souvenir shop.

Open: weekends Easter to October, daily July and August.

Directions: in the town of Bo'ness. Leave M9 at Junction 3 or 5, then follow brown tourist signs.

On show is a large collection, from 1899, of cars, bicycles, motor cycles and commercials. There is also a large collection of period advertising, posters and enamel signs.

Open: March-November - open daily 11am to 4pm. December-February - weekends 11am to 3pm or by special appointment.

Directions: off A198 near Aberlady. Two miles from A1.

227

FHG
·K·U·P·E·R·A·R·D·
**READERS'
OFFER
2008**

CLYDEBUILT SCOTTISH MARITIME MUSEUM
Braehead Shopping Centre, King's Inch Road,
Glasgow G51 4BN
Tel: 0141-886 1013 • Fax: 0141-886 1015
e-mail: clydebuilt@scotmaritime.org.uk
www.scottishmaritimemuseum.org

*HALF PRICE admission for up to 4 persons.
Valid during 2008.*

NOT TO BE USED IN CONJUNCTION WITH ANY OTHER OFFER

FHG
·K·U·P·E·R·A·R·D·
**READERS'
OFFER
2008**

SPEYSIDE HEATHER GARDEN & VISITOR CENTRE
Speyside Heather Centre, Dulnain Bridge,
Inverness-shire PH26 3PA
Tel: 01479 851359 • Fax: 01479 851396
e-mail: enquiries@heathercentre.com
www.heathercentre.com

Speyside HEATHER GARDEN

*FREE entry to 'Heather Story' exhibition
Valid during 2008*

NOT TO BE USED IN CONJUNCTION WITH ANY OTHER OFFER

FHG
·K·U·P·E·R·A·R·D·
**READERS'
OFFER
2008**

LLANBERIS LAKE RAILWAY
Gilfach Ddu, Llanberis,
Gwynedd LL55 4TY
Tel: 01286 870549
e-mail: info@lake-railway.co.uk
www.lake-railway.co.uk

*One pet travels FREE with each full fare paying adult
Valid Easter to October 2008*

NOT TO BE USED IN CONJUNCTION WITH ANY OTHER OFFER

FHG
·K·U·P·E·R·A·R·D·
**READERS'
OFFER
2008**

ANIMALARIUM
Borth,
Ceredigion
SY24 5NA
Tel: 01970 871224
www.animalarium.co.uk

*FREE child with full paying adult.
Valid during 2008.*

NOT TO BE USED IN CONJUNCTION WITH ANY OTHER OFFER

228

The story of Glasgow and the River Clyde brought vividly to life using AV, hands-on and interactive techniques. You can navigate your own ship, safely load your cargo, operate an engine, and go aboard the 130-year-old coaster 'Kyles'. Ideal for kids young and old wanting an exciting day out. New - The Clyde's Navy.

Open: 10am to 5.30pm daily

Directions: Green Car Park near M&S at Braehead Shopping Centre.

Award-winning attraction with unique 'Heather Story' exhibition, gallery, giftshop, large garden centre selling 300 different heathers, antique shop, children's play area and famous Clootie Dumpling restaurant.

Open: all year except Christmas Day.

Directions: just off A95 between Aviemore and Grantown-on-Spey.

A 60-minute ride along the shores of beautiful Padarn Lake behind a quaint historic steam engine. Magnificent views of the mountains from lakeside picnic spots.

DOGS MUST BE KEPT ON LEAD AT ALL TIMES ON TRAIN

Open: most days Easter to October. Free timetable leaflet on request.

Directions: just off A4086 Caernarfon to Capel Curig road at Llanberis; follow 'Country Park' signs.

A collection of unusual and interesting animals, including breeding pairs and colonies of exotic and endangered species whose natural environment is under threat. Many were unwanted exotic pets or came from other zoos.

Open: 10am - 6pm April to October

Directions: only a short walk from the railway station and beach in Borth, which lies between Aberystwyth and Machynlleth.

Visit the FHG website
www.holidayguides.com
for details of the wide choice of accommodation

featured in the full range of FHG titles

Mini-rainforest full of tropical plants and exotic butterflies. *Personal attention of the owner, Mr John Devereux. Gift shop, cafe, video room, exhibition. Suitable for disabled visitors. VisitWales Quality Assured Visitor Attraction.*

PETS NOT ALLOWED IN TROPICAL HOUSE ONLY

Open: daily Easter to end October 10.30am to 5pm

Directions: West Wales, 7 miles north of Cardigan off Aberystwyth road. Follow brown tourist signs on A487.

FHG GUIDES, ABBEY MILL BUSINESS CENTRE, PAISLEY PA1 1TJ • www.holidayguides.com

---

Journey through the lanes of cycle history and see bicycles from Boneshakers and Penny Farthings up to modern Raleigh cycles. Over 250 machines on display

PETS MUST BE KEPT ON LEADS

Open: 1st March to 1st November daily 10am onwards.

Directions: brown signs to car park. Town centre attraction.

FHG GUIDES, ABBEY MILL BUSINESS CENTRE, PAISLEY PA1 1TJ • www.holidayguides.com

---

Make a pit stop whatever the weather! Join an ex-miner on a tour of discovery, ride the cage to pit bottom and take a thrilling ride back to the surface. Multi-media presentations, period village street, children's adventure play area, restaurant and gift shop. Disabled access with assistance.

Open: Open daily 10am to 6pm (last tour 4pm). Closed Mondays Oct - Easter, also Dec 25th to early Jan.

Directions: Exit Junction 32 M4, signposted from A470 Pontypridd. Trehafod is located between Pontypridd and Porth.

FHG GUIDES, ABBEY MILL BUSINESS CENTRE, PAISLEY PA1 1TJ • www.holidayguides.com

Please note

3: 9781857334203	ISBN 13: 9781857334128	ISBN 13: 9781857334173	ISBN 13: 9781857334197	ISBN 13: 9781857334180	ISBN 13: 9781857334210
-07 £12.95	New £12.95	NEW £12.95	Sept 2007 £12.95	Sept 2007 £12.95	Jan 2008 £12.95
789614155014)					

chic series are the definitive guides to the world's most luxurious and alluring hotels. The
erties featured—whether a city hotel, a beachside resort or a rustic hacienda—have been
en for their individuality and chic appeal.

hts into the essence of each property help readers decide on the one that best suits their needs
preferences. A fact-packed panel summarises each hotel's facilities and nearby attractions.

thechicseries

raordinary destinations. Incomparable accommodations. Exceptional advice.
n discerning travellers who have found everything they desire in the chic series
vel guides: hot properties, stunning photography and brilliant tips on where to go
how to do it in some of the worlds chicest locations.

: 9781857334159	ISBN 13: 9781857334104	ISBN 13: 9781857334081	ISBN 13: 9781857334067	ISBN 13: 9781857334135

9781857334111	ISBN 13: 9781857334050	ISBN 13: 9781857334098	ISBN 13: 9781857334166	ISBN 13: 9781857334142

Order any chic guide via the Kuperard website and receive free postage on any
quantity of guides. Visit www.kuperard.co.uk to see the full range in the
series and type in the following promotional code chic2.
Or call us on 0208 446 2440 and quote the same code.

All titles are paperback priced £12.95

CULTURE SMART ! a quick guide to customs and etiquette

THE SMARTER WAY TO TRAVEL

In China it's rude to be late. In France it's rude to be on time. Never be unpleasant in Thailand, but in Russia, smiling at strangers may be seen as a sign of stupidity. Culture Smart! guides create steps towards understanding the people and instantly enriches your experience abroad.

Books are priced £6.95 and published by Kuperard. Order any Culture Smart! guide via the Kuperard website and receive free postage on any quantity of guides. Visit www.kuperard.co.uk and type in the following promotional code: CSG1, or call us on 0208 446 2440 and quote the same code.

Fall 2007 Titles

| 978-1-85733-353-4 | 978-1-85733-349-7 | 978-1-85733-350-3 | 978-1-85733-35 |

| 9781857333282 | 9781857333107 | 9781857333473 | 9781857333220 | 9781857333404 | 9781857333237 | 9781857333114 | 978185733 |

| 9781857333046 | 9781857333244 | 9781857333381 | 9781857333343 | 9781857333251 | 9781857333428 | 9781857333640 | 978185733 |

| 9781857333060 | 9781857333695 | 9781857333480 | 9781857333688 | 9781857333350 | 9781857333053 | 9781857333435 | 978185733 |

| 9781857333442 | 9781857333169 | 9781857333091 | 9781857333657 | 9781857333664 | 9781857333374 | 9781857333121 | 978185733 |

| 9781857333312 | 9781857333398 | 9781857333367 | 9781857333176 | 9781857333671 | 9781857333329 | 9781857333183 | 978185733 |

| 9781857333152 | 9781857333190 | 9781857333206 | 9781857333145 | 9781857333268 | 9781857333275 | 9781857333213 | 978185733 |

Index of Towns and Counties

Ratings & Awards

For the first time ever the AA, VisitBritain, VisitScotland, and the Wales Tourist Board will use a single method of assessing and rating serviced accommodation. Irrespective of which organisation inspects an establishment the rating awarded will be the same, using a common set of standards, giving a clear guide of what to expect. The RAC is no longer operating an Hotel inspection and accreditation business.

Accommodation Standards: Star Grading Scheme

Using a scale of 1-5 stars the objective quality ratings give a clear indication of accommodation standard, cleanliness, ambience, hospitality, service and food, This shows the full range of standards suitable for every budget and preference, and allows visitors to distinguish between the quality of accommodation and facilities on offer in different establishments. All types of board and self-catering accommodation are covered, including hotels, B&Bs, holiday parks, campus accommodation, hostels, caravans and camping, and boats.

VisitBritain and the regional tourist boards, enjoyEngland.com, VisitScotland and VisitWales, and the AA have full details of the grading system on their websites

The more stars, the higher level of quality

★★★★★
exceptional quality, with a degree of luxury

★★★★
excellent standard throughout

★★★
very good level of quality and comfort

★★
good quality, well presented and well run

★
acceptable quality; simple, practical, no frills

National Accessible Scheme

If you have particular mobility, visual or hearing needs, look out for the National Accessible Scheme. You can be confident of finding accommodation or attractions that meet your needs by looking for the following symbols.

 Typically suitable for a person with sufficient mobility to climb a flight of steps but would benefit from fixtures and fittings to aid balance

 Typically suitable for a person with restricted walking ability and for those that may need to use a wheelchair some of the time and can negotiate a maximum of three steps

 Typically suitable for a person who depends on the use of a wheelchair and transfers unaided to and from the wheelchair in a seated position. This person may be an independent traveller

 Typically suitable for a person who depends on the use of a wheelchair in a seated position. This person also requires personal or mechanical assistance (eg carer, hoist).

Looking for Holiday Accommodation?

for details of hundreds of properties throughout the UK, visit our website

www.holidayguides.com

FHG Guides Ltd have a large range of attractive
holiday accommodation guides for all kinds of holiday opportunities throughout Britain.
They also make useful gifts at any time of year.
Our guides are available in most bookshops and larger newsagents but we will be happy
to post you a copy direct if you have any difficulty. POST FREE for addresses in the UK.
We will also post abroad but have to charge separately for post or freight.

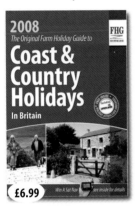

**The original
Farm Holiday Guide to
COAST & COUNTRY HOLIDAYS**
in England, Scotland, Wales and
Channel Islands. Board, Self-
catering, Caravans/Camping,
Activity Holidays.

**Recommended
INNS & PUBS of Britain**
Pubs, Inns and small hotels.

**BRITAIN'S BEST LEISURE
& RELAXATION GUIDE**
A quick-reference general guide
for all kinds of holidays.

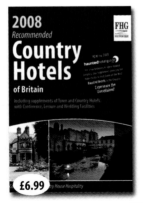

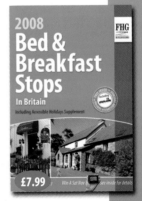

**The Original
PETS WELCOME!**
The bestselling guide to
holidays for pet owners
and their pets.

**Recommended
COUNTRY HOTELS
of Britain**
Including Country Houses, for the
discriminating.

BED & BREAKFAST STOPS
Over 1000 friendly and
comfortable overnight stops.
Non-smoking, Disabled and
Special Diets Suplements..

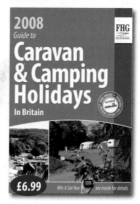

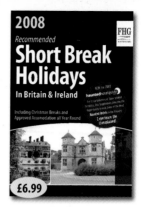

CHILDREN WELCOME!
Family Holidays and
Days Out guide.
Family holidays with details of
amenities for children and
babies.

The FHG Guide to
CARAVAN & CAMPING
HOLIDAYS
Caravans for hire, sites and
holiday parks and centres.

Recommended
SHORT BREAK HOLIDAYS
IN BRITAIN & IRELAND
"Approved" accommodation for
quality bargain breaks.

The GOLF GUIDE – *Where to play Where to stay*
In association with GOLF MONTHLY. Over 2800 golf
courses in Britain with convenient accommodation.
Holiday Golf in France, Portugal, Spain, USA and Thailand.

£9.99

Tick your choice above and send your order and payment to

FHG Guides Ltd. Abbey Mill Business Centre
Seedhill, Paisley, Scotland PA1 1TJ
TEL: 0141- 887 0428 • FAX: 0141- 889 7204
e-mail: admin@fhguides.co.uk

Deduct 10% for 2/3 titles or copies; 20% for 4 or more.

Send to: NAME ....

           ADDRESS ....

           ....

           ....

           POST CODE ....

I enclose Cheque/Postal Order for £ ....

           SIGNATURE ....DATE ....

Please complete the following to help us improve the service we provide.

How did you find out about our guides?:

☐Press   ☐Magazines   ☐TV/Radio   ☐Family/Friend   ☐Other